# Target
## Get back on track

**Edexcel GCSE (9–1)**
# History

## Crime and punishment through time, c1000–present

### Laura Goodyear

Pearson

Published by Pearson Education Limited, 80 Strand, London, WC2R ORL.

www.pearsonschoolsandfecolleges.co.uk

Copies of official specifications for all Pearson qualifications may be found on the website: qualifications.pearson.com

Text © Pearson Education Limited 2018
Produced by Out of House Publishing Solutions
Typeset by Newgen KnowledgeWorks Pvt. Ltd., Chennai, India

The right of Laura Goodyear to be identified as author of this work has been asserted by her in accordance with the Copyright, Designs and Patents Act 1988.

First published 2018

21 20 19 18
10 9 8 7 6 5 4 3 2 1

**British Library Cataloguing in Publication Data**
A catalogue record for this book is available from the British Library

ISBN 978 0 435 189457

**Acknowledgements**
The author and publisher would like to thank the following individuals and organisations for their kind permission to reproduce copyright material.

**Page 25**
https://www.nationalarchives.gov.uk/documents/education/jacktheripper.pdf , © Crown copyright 2013, Source: The National Archives licensed under the Open Government License v.3.0.

**Photographs**
(Key: b-bottom; c-centre; l-left; r-right; t-top)

**Alamy Stock Photo:** Photo Researchers/Science History Images 29,
**Mary Evans:** © Illustrated London News Ltd 11, 12, 19, TopFoto.co.uk: 17

All other images © Pearson Education

**Note from the publisher**
Pearson has robust editorial processes, including answer and fact checks, to ensure the accuracy of the content in this publication, and every effort is made to ensure this publication is free of errors. We are, however, only human, and occasionally errors do occur. Pearson is not liable for any misunderstandings that arise as a result of errors in this publication, but it is our priority to ensure that the content is accurate. If you spot an error, please do contact us at resourcescorrections@pearson.com so we can make sure it is corrected.

# Contents

# ① Selecting and applying your own knowledge

This unit will help you to identify relevant features of a topic and build on these features with details from your own knowledge. The skills you will build are to:

- choose historical knowledge based on what the question is asking you
- decide how much of your own historical knowledge you need to include in an answer
- use your own historical knowledge effectively.

The skill of selecting and applying your own knowledge is important for all the questions you might be asked in your History GCSE.

In the exam, you will also be asked to tackle questions such as the one below. This unit will prepare you to write your own response to this exam-style question:

**Exam-style question**

Describe **two** features of immigration into Whitechapel.

Feature 1

..................................................................................................................................................

..................................................................................................................................................

Feature 2

..................................................................................................................................................

..................................................................................................................................................

(4 marks)

The three key questions in the **skills boosts** will help you to decide what historical knowledge you need when you are answering Paper 1 history questions.

**① How do I identify relevant features?**  **② How do I add relevant detail?**  **③ How do I know how much to write?**

Look at the student response to the exam-style question below:

**Exam-style question**

Describe **two** features of immigration into Whitechapel.

> During the 1840s many young Irishmen arrived in London on their way to America. When money ran out, they stayed and worked as navvies. These were labourers on the canals, roads and railways. Many settled in Whitechapel and this made overcrowding worse. In 1881 the Tsar of Russia was assassinated and people blamed Jewish people, so many of them fled to London. They had a very different culture and they often kept themselves separate from the rest of the Whitechapel community.

(**1**) Highlight 🖉 any features the student has identified.

(**2**) Cross out (cat) the information in the student answer that is not necessary to answer the question.

(**3**) For each feature identified, the student gives one extra detail to expand the information. Try to identify 🖉 this extra detail for each feature.

Feature 1 ..............................................................................................................................

..............................................................................................................................

..............................................................................................................................

Feature 2 ..............................................................................................................................

..............................................................................................................................

..............................................................................................................................

# Tensions in Whitechapel

This unit uses the theme of tensions in Whitechapel to build your skills in selecting and applying your own knowledge. If you need to review your knowledge of this theme, work through these pages.

**(1)** Read the statements about the environment of Whitechapel below and tick ✓ the correct ones.

**a** Whitechapel was one of the country's poorest districts, located in West London.

**b** Londoners shared the district with immigrants of Irish and Jewish descent.

**c** Each house was divided into several apartments.

**d** There would never be more than one family in each apartment.

**(2)** Look at the crimes and social problems listed in the word box. Circle Ⓐ the ones most closely associated with unemployment in Whitechapel.

| theft of personal property | domestic abuse | stealing/robbery |
| --- | --- | --- |
| assaults on women | disorder in the streets | begging |
| political agitation | gang violence | disruptive behaviour |

**(3)** Draw ✎ lines linking a social group living in Whitechapel to a description of it.

A Irish

B Jewish

C Socialists

D Anarchists

**a** Immigrant population which grew during the 1880s. Most were fleeing Eastern Europe after being blamed for the assassination of the Tsar of Russia.

**b** A potentially revolutionary group who wanted to bring down the capitalist system. Their political party, the SDF, was formed to represent agricultural and industrial labourers.

**c** A potentially revolutionary group who thought the answer to Europe's social and economic problems was to overthrow the existing monarchs. Britain was normally where leaders fled to when escaping arrest in their own country.

**d** Immigrant population which expanded rapidly from the 1840s. Usually young men with plans to continue on to America but when money ran out they stayed and worked as navvies – labourers on canals, roads and railways.

④ Draw ✎ lines linking each of the descriptions of tensions in Whitechapel to the element of the population that was thought to be causing it.

**A** This group would often work for 16 to 18 hours a day and made goods very cheaply. This drove the price of the goods down, which was very unpopular with other workers.

**a** Anarchists

**B** This group was often linked to the Fenians, a terrorist organisation fighting for independence from British rule.

**b** Irish

**C** Violent revolutionary action had been happening in continental Europe. The British press exaggerated the extent of bomb attacks, but in London many people were assuming anyone with an Eastern European accent was a threat.

**c** Socialists

**D** They used the Jack the Ripper case to highlight the stupidity of the Metropolitan Police and the government in the hope of an SDF councillor being elected in the area.

**d** Jewish

⑤ Existing communities in Whitechapel were fearful of the effect the arrival of immigrants and different social groups in their community might have. Look at the speech bubbles and groups listed below. Write ✎ the name of the group next to the comment being made about them.

| Jewish | Irish | Socialists | Anarchists |

**a**

They are putting my job at risk!

...................................................

**b**

They might set off a bomb!

...................................................

**c**

They don't speak English so I don't know what they are saying!

...................................................

**d**

They're always causing problems with the police!

...................................................

**How do I identify relevant features?**

In order to answer relevantly, you will need to identify two features. You will therefore need to:

- read the question and highlight the topic of Crime and policing in Whitechapel
- make a list of features of this topic from your own knowledge.

Look at the two exam-style questions below:

A

**Exam-style question**

Describe **two** features of Jewish immigration to Whitechapel.

Feature 1 ...................................................................

...................................................................

Feature 2 ...................................................................

...................................................................

(4 marks)

B

**Exam-style question**

Describe **two** features of anarchism in Whitechapel.

Feature 1 ...................................................................

...................................................................

Feature 2 ...................................................................

...................................................................

(4 marks)

① Highlight ✏ the 'topic' parts of questions A and B.

② ⓐ The text you have highlighted in the exam-style questions above tells you what knowledge to use to describe **relevant** features. Look at the features described below and sort them into the table under the correct heading. ✏

| Question A | Question B |
|---|---|
|  |  |
|  |  |
|  |  |
|  |  |

| Were resented by the local workers of Whitechapel | Were often considered to be terrorists |
|---|---|

| Often came to Britain fleeing arrest | Came mainly from Eastern Europe, fleeing persecution |
|---|---|

ⓑ Add ✏ one more feature for each question.

**Unit 1 Selecting and applying your own knowledge** 5

## 2 How do I add relevant detail?

It is necessary to support the feature you have identified with relevant details to develop your answer.

(1) The table below shows each of the features identified for the two exam-style questions on the previous page. Draw 🖉 lines linking the feature to its supporting detail.

Feature                                          Supporting detail

A Were resented by the local workers of Whitechapel

a In 1881 the Russian Tsar had been assassinated and they were blamed. The Russian government started to attack them so they fled to Britain to avoid persecution.

B Came mainly from Eastern Europe, fleeing persecution

b Their revolutionary political ideas were believed to be a threat to law and order in Britain.

C Often came to Britain fleeing arrest

c Compared to the poor working class living in Whitechapel they seemed to find employment easily and were often successful in business.

D Were often considered to be terrorists

d This threat of arrest was a result of their revolutionary attempts to overthrow existing governments.

(2) Now write 🖉 the two features you added of your own in (2) (b) of page 5 and add a supporting detail to each to develop your description.

| My feature | Supporting detail |
| --- | --- |
| Exam-style question A: | |
| Exam-style question B: | |

# 3 How do I know how much to write?

Question 1 is worth just 4 marks, so each relevant feature you identify will score a mark and each relevant supporting detail will score a mark. This means full marks can be achieved with just four sentences.

(1) You are now going to use the relevant features and the details that have been identified to practise writing an answer to the following exam-style questions. Fill in ✎ the tables to help you to see what you need to write for each answer.

Question A:

**Exam-style question**

Describe **two** features of Jewish immigration to Whitechapel.

| | |
|---|---|
| Sentence 1 (feature 1) | |
| Sentence 2 (supporting detail) | |
| Sentence 3 (feature 2) | |
| Sentence 4 (supporting detail) | |

Question B:

**Exam-style question**

Describe **two** features of anarchism in Whitechapel.

| | |
|---|---|
| Sentence 1 (feature 1) | |
| Sentence 2 (supporting detail) | |
| Sentence 3 (feature 2) | |
| Sentence 4 (supporting detail) | |

# Sample response

Read the exam-style question below and the student response that follows.

**Exam-style question**

Describe **two** features of socialism in Whitechapel.

Feature 1 ...................................................................................................................................

...................................................................................................................................................

...................................................................................................................................................

...................................................................................................................................................

Feature 2 ...................................................................................................................................

...................................................................................................................................................

...................................................................................................................................................

...................................................................................................................................................

(4 marks)

Socialists wanted to end the capitalist system in Britain to create a fairer spread of wealth.
They believed it was unfair that only a few people benefited from the money made by
industry. Capitalism was when businesses were privately owned and investors could decide how
the money made from that industry was used. The first socialist party had been founded in
Britain in 1881 and there was hope that they may be able to get a local councillor elected in
Whitechapel due to the large number of working class residents there, whom they represented.

/4

(1) Circle (A) the topic in the exam-style question.

(2) Annotate the answer highlighting (✐) one feature and its supporting detail in one colour and the
second feature and its supporting detail in another. To help you, you could write (✐) your answer
into the exam-style question.

(3) Give the answer a score out of 4. (✐)

(4) Circle (A) and label (✐) the feature which is not relevant.

(5) Write (✐) an additional feature that might be more relevant to this question. How would you
support it?

Feature ......................................................................................................................................

...................................................................................................................................................

Supporting detail ......................................................................................................................

...................................................................................................................................................

...................................................................................................................................................

# Your turn!

Now it is your turn to try to answer an exam-style question.

**Exam-style question**

Describe **two** features of the Irish immigrant community in Whitechapel.

(**1**) Highlight 🖉 the topic from which you must select your features.

(**2**) List 🖉 two features relevant to this topic.

1 .............................................................................................................................
.............................................................................................................................

2 .............................................................................................................................
.............................................................................................................................

(**3**) Use the table below to plan 🖉 a relevant detail to support each feature.

| | |
|---|---|
| 1 | |
| 2 | |

(**4**) Now write 🖉 your answer as a descriptive paragraph of four sentences.

Feature 1

.............................................................................................................................
.............................................................................................................................

Supporting detail

.............................................................................................................................
.............................................................................................................................
.............................................................................................................................

Feature 2

.............................................................................................................................
.............................................................................................................................

Supporting detail

.............................................................................................................................
.............................................................................................................................
.............................................................................................................................

**Unit 1 Selecting and applying your own knowledge** 9

# Review your skills

## Check up

Review your response to the exam-style question on page 9. Tick ✓ the column below to show how well you think you have done each of the following.

|  | Had a go ✓ | Nearly there ✓ | Got it! ✓ |
|---|---|---|---|
| identified the 'topic' in the question to ensure features are relevant | ☐ | ☐ | ☐ |
| selected two features and added relevant detail | ☐ | ☐ | ☐ |
| worked out how much to write | ☐ | ☐ | ☐ |

## Need more practice?

If you want to practise another exam-style question, have a go 🖉 at the one below.

**Exam-style question**

Describe **two** features of poverty in Whitechapel.

Feature 1 .................................................................................................................

................................................................................................................................

................................................................................................................................

................................................................................................................................

Feature 2 .................................................................................................................

................................................................................................................................

................................................................................................................................

................................................................................................................................

(4 marks)

How confident do you feel about each of these **skills**? Colour 🖉 in the bars.

**1** How do I identify relevant features?

**2** How do I add relevant detail?

**3** How do I know how much to write?

# ② Following up a source

This unit will help you learn and practise how to select interesting details from a source that you would like to know more about, and then plan a follow-up enquiry around it.

The skills you will build are to:

- select details from sources that could be followed up
- ask questions about source details
- suggest valid methods of answering your questions.

In the exam, you will also be asked to tackle questions such as the one below. This unit will prepare you to write your own response to this exam-style question.

**Exam-style question**

Study Source A

How could you follow up Source A to find out more about what was done to help the poor in Whitechapel? In your answer you must give the question you would ask and the type of source you could use.

Complete the table below.                                                                        (4 marks)

Detail in Source A that I would follow up: ................................................................

Question I would ask: ................................................................

What type of source I could use: ................................................................

How this might help answer my question: ................................................................

**Source A** *Illustration of starving women and children in London, 1889.*

Notice the types of questions you are being asked in this question.

? What detail would I follow up on?

? What further questions would I ask?

? What type of source could I use to answer these?

? How might this answer my question?

The three key questions in the **skills boosts** will help you answer the four questions above.

 **1** How do I identify details in the source?

 **2** How do I ask good questions about the source?

 **3** How do I select valid methods of answering my question?

Here are some questions you might consider when looking at Source A.

**1** | **What aspect of crime and punishment is being demonstrated?** This image is of starving women and children in Whitechapel; therefore it is telling us about the issue of poverty which often led to crimes being committed.

**4** | **What is the provenance?** This tells us a bit about the source, ideally who produced it, and when and where it was produced. When the source is a photograph or picture, it may provide you with a little more detail about what you are looking at.

**Source A** Illustration of starving women and children in London, 1889.

**2** | **What question(s) do you still have about the source?** For example, you might want to know how widespread poverty was in Whitechapel or whether it led to an increase in crime rates and, if it did, what types of crime.

**3** | **Where might you find further evidence?** Evidence of parliamentary committees, newspaper reports, workhouse records, police records, etc.

(1) (a) Write down 🖊 one of the questions you would like to ask to follow up this source.

........................................................................

........................................................................

........................................................................

........................................................................

(b) Note down 🖊 what type of source you think is most likely to answer your question.

........................................................................

........................................................................

........................................................................

........................................................................

(c) Why do you think this is most likely to provide you with an answer? 🖊

........................................................................

........................................................................

........................................................................

........................................................................

........................................................................

# Policing: techniques and effectiveness

This unit uses the theme of the techniques and effectiveness of policing to build your skills in following up a source. If you need to review your knowledge of this theme, work through these pages.

① **a** Highlight ✐ three **issues** arising from the arrival of Irish immigrants.

**b** Circle Ⓐ three **issues** arising from the arrival of Jewish immigrants.

| | | | |
|---|---|---|---|
| They settled in areas near the river as they tried to find work as navvies. | They were revolutionaries seeking refuge in Whitechapel. They threatened the stability of government. | The people of Whitechapel resented their cultural differences and different attitudes towards work and business. | They came from Eastern Europe as a result of their persecution following the assassination of the Russian Tsar. |
| They were a large social group and chose to live separately from the rest of the Whitechapel community. | Violence often broke out between them, caused by alcohol and competition over work. | Some were members of Fenian groups. The Fenians were a terrorist movement looking to achieve independence for Ireland. | They were revolutionaries seeking refuge in Whitechapel. They threatened the capitalist system in Britain. |

② **a** Write ✐ a number from 1 to 4 in the box below each technique in order to demonstrate what you believe to be the most and least effective. (1 for the most to 4 for the least effective.)

**b** Now link ✐ the groups in the left-hand column to the descriptions in the right-hand column.

| | |
|---|---|
| **A** Following up direct leads from the public ☐ | **a** It was suggested that the marks on one victim's body indicated the killer was left-handed and had some knowledge of anatomy. |
| **B** Evidence from post mortems ☐ | **b** Used because the police were not allowed to offer money for information but hoped this would encourage the poor to come forward with information and clues. |
| **C** Indirect leads from articles written by investigating journalists ☐ | **c** People would report crimes that had a possible connection to the Whitechapel murders, which would then be investigated further by police. |
| **D** Setting up soup kitchens ☐ | **d** The *Manchester Guardian* suggested it could be a killer local to Manchester called Leather Apron. |

## Remember this?

**Methods used in police inquiry**

- Following up evidence from post mortems
- Following up direct leads
- Following up indirect leads from articles by investigating journalists
- Visiting soup kitchens

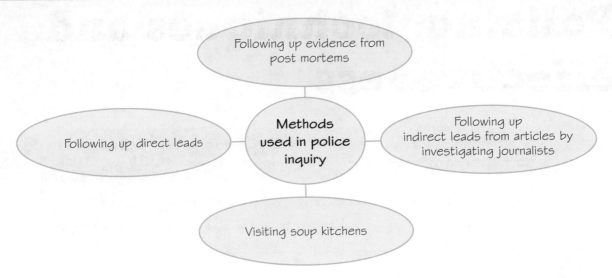

**3** On the diagram above:

- **a** Highlight the methods used to identify the victims.
- **b** Underline the methods used to track possible suspects.
- **c** Circle the methods used to get possible witnesses to come forward.

**4** **a** The statements listed below (A–F) describe the problems affecting the police investigation. Highlight the problems caused by the media in one colour and the problems related to a lack of forensic techniques in another. Fill in the colour code key to mark your colours.

**Colour code:** Media ☐ Lack of forensic techniques ☐

**A** It was impossible to distinguish between animal and human blood.

**B** Had to rely on clues such as clothing and people reporting missing persons to identify victims.

**C** Police were sent over 300 letters and postcards by men claiming to be the murderer. Too many leads to follow up each effectively and took up police time.

**D** If a witness gave a description police had no way of identifying the person described.

**E** Bloodhounds were the only method of tracking criminals. Their use was based on the dog's ability to track the smell of one person's blood through the streets of London.

**F** Public accusations of Jewish and Irish people potentially led to greater disorder in Whitechapel, which the police would have to deal with.

**a** The development of fingerprinting methods to detect criminals.

**b** The discovery of different blood groups.

**c** The Bertillon System (1893). Combined physical measurements and photographs of known criminals to create a database from which police could check the identity of potential suspects.

**b** The solutions to some of the problems are shown in boxes (**a**–**c**) around the central statements. Link and circle these solutions to the problems they solved.

# How do I identify details in the source?

In order to start following up a source for an enquiry, you need to understand what the source is about and identify relevant details.

Look at the exam-style question and source below.

**Exam-style question**

How could you follow up Source B to find out more about public attitudes to the police in Whitechapel?

**Source B** | *A story published in* The Illustrated Police News, *2 June 1883, about a gang attack on a Whitechapel policeman.*

**Savage Attack Upon A Policeman**

John Harris, Jane Reynolds and Alfred Lindsey were charged in committing a murderous assault on Dennis Mortimer, a constable... Constable Mortimer heard loud cries of 'Stop him!' and as he tackled Harris a mob of young ruffians collected around him and commenced pelting him with stones and hitting him with sticks. Mortimer made strenuous efforts to protect himself, but on drawing his truncheon, according to a witness, the female Reynolds wrenched it from his hand and struck him on the side of the head with it, and another girl also hit him about the head. The prisoner and his gang made their escape, leaving the constable unconscious.

(1) Make sure the detail you select to follow up is relevant to the focus of the question (highlighted above). From your own knowledge, what details about 'public attitudes to police in Whitechapel' would you expect to find in a source? ✏

..................................................................................................................................................................

..................................................................................................................................................................

(2) Read the following statements. Then tick ✓ which are aspects of public attitudes towards the police in Whitechapel mentioned by the source.

A  Assault against a police officer

B  Gangs who opposed the authority of the police

D  Grouping together to resist arrest

C  That the police were a heavy handed and violent force

> The selected detail should also prompt further questions, for example: Which gangs? How did they oppose authority? You can then follow up using different source material.

(3) Choose one of the statements you ticked in **2** and explain why it could be described as a public attitude towards the police. ✏

> You must select just one detail from the source for this exam question, so select the relevant detail you feel most confident to follow up.

..................................................................................................................................................................

..................................................................................................................................................................

..................................................................................................................................................................

..................................................................................................................................................................

..................................................................................................................................................................

..................................................................................................................................................................

**How do I ask good questions about the source?**

Historians will always use as many sources as possible because every source has its own strengths and weaknesses. Considering these strengths and weaknesses will help you to ask good questions when following up a source.

Look at this exam-style question and source below.

**Exam-style question**

How could you follow up Source C to find out more about the accuracy of criminal statistics in telling us about crime in Whitechapel in the 1890s? In your answer, you must give the question you would ask and the type of source you could use.

**Source C** From a national report by a government committee on criminal statistics in 1895. The committee is reporting on problems in the police tables of crimes and convictions, which were published each year.

The figures have been prepared by the police with great care, but some forces have proceeded on one basis and others on another. The making of an attendance order [issued when a parent failed to send a child to school] was treated as a conviction by 121 police forces and excluded from the returns by 27. This alone added about 20,000 convictions a year to the tables, where there was in fact no conviction.

| police figures | forensic investigation | immigration | convictions | statistics |
| --- | --- | --- | --- | --- |

(1) Circle (A) all the aspects of crime mentioned in the source and link them (✎) to the correct label.

(2) (a) Write (✎) a detail from Source C that you would like to follow up.

.................................................................................................................................

.................................................................................................................................

(b) For the detail you have chosen, write (✎) **three** questions using the starters below in order to explore it further:

Why .............................................................................................................................

How .............................................................................................................................

Where ..........................................................................................................................

(c) Which of your three questions above would you choose to follow up the source and why? (✎)

.................................................................................................................................

.................................................................................................................................

.................................................................................................................................

# ③ How do I select valid methods of answering my question?

When answering a question that requires you to follow up a source, you must select a source to help you answer the question you have set yourself.

Look at the exam-style question and related source below.

**Exam-style question**

How could you follow up Source D to find out more about the effectiveness of the use of bloodhounds in police investigations? In your answer, you must give the question you would ask and the type of source you could use.

**Source D** The Penny Illustrated Paper *article on Jack the Ripper. Sir Charles Warren's new criminal trackers: Mr Brough's bloodhounds being trained. Charles Warren was the Police Commissioner during the period of the Whitechapel murders in 1888.*

① Underline Ⓐ the section of the exam-style question that identifies the aspect of crime and policing in Whitechapel being discussed.

② Write down ✎ **one** new question of your own, related to a detail in the source.

③ ⓐ Consider the likely nature, origin and purpose of each source in the table and score ✎ each one for usefulness. (3 = very useful, 0 = not useful at all.)

| Source | Nature (Answers question?) | Origin (Who by? Reliable?) | Purpose (Why written? Reliable?) | ✓ |
|---|---|---|---|---|
| A letter by Warren asking about ability of bloodhounds to follow scent | /3 | /3 | /3 | |
| Police statistic regarding success rate of bloodhounds | /3 | /3 | /3 | |
| Memoirs of a beat constable | /3 | /3 | /3 | |

ⓑ In the last column, tick ✓ the source you think would be most useful in answering your own new question from ②.

ⓒ Explain ✎ how the type of source you have chosen could help you answer your own new question from ②.

Source: ............................................................................................................

I believe this will be able to answer my question because: ............................

.........................................................................................................................

.........................................................................................................................

# Sample response

Read the source, exam-style question and student answer below.

**Source E** *From a report in the* East London Advertiser *newspaper, published 15 September 1888. The writer is commenting on Metropolitan Police Commissioner, Sir Charles Warren's decision to bring in soldiers to help police in Whitechapel.*

The double stupidity of weakening his detective force and strengthening his ordinary police force from reserves and the military destroys two safeguards of a community. It deprives it of a specially trained force of men with brainpower specially adapted for detective work and it takes away the old community constable, to be replaced by a man with a few years' military service, but with no other qualification for serving the public. Nothing has indeed been more characteristic of the hunt for the Whitechapel murderer than the lack of local knowledge displayed by the police. They seem to know little of the dark alleyways of the neighbourhood and still less of the bad characters who swarm through them.

## Exam-style question

**Study Source E.**

How could you follow up Source E to find out more about how efficient policing in Whitechapel was in 1888? In your answer, you must give the question you would ask and the type of source you could use.

Complete the table below. **(4 marks)**

Detail in Source E that I would follow up:

*the... stupidity of strengthening his ordinary police force from reserves and the military*

Question I would ask:

*What impact did the extra men have on the investigation?*

What type of source I could use:

*Crime reports after September 1888*

How this might help answer my question:

*Crime reports might show whether there was a fall in overall crime rates in Whitechapel as the police would have more capacity to follow up leads. Alternatively they may show an increase in reactions against a military presence instead of usual 'bobbies'.*

(1) Highlight 🖉 the section in the source which outlines the efficiency of policing in Whitechapel in 1888.

(2) Note down 🖉 how you might improve the question this student asks or use your own knowledge to give an alternative question.

......................................................................................................................................................

(3) Can you think of a better source to answer the student's question? Write 🖉 your suggestion below.

......................................................................................................................................................

(4) Explain why 🖉 you think your source would be better by saying how it might help answer the question.

......................................................................................................................................................

......................................................................................................................................................

# Your turn!

①  Now you are going to write ✐ your own answer to this exam-style question.

**Exam-style question**

Study Source A.

How could you follow up Source A to find out more about what was done to help the poor in Whitechapel? In your answer you must give the question you would ask and the type of source you could use.

Complete the table below.                                                          **(4 marks)**

Detail in Source A that I would follow up:

........................................................................................................................

........................................................................................................................

........................................................................................................................

Question I would ask:

........................................................................................................................

........................................................................................................................

........................................................................................................................

What type of source I could use:

........................................................................................................................

........................................................................................................................

........................................................................................................................

How this might help answer my question:

........................................................................................................................

........................................................................................................................

........................................................................................................................

**Source A**    *Illustration of starving women and children in London, 1889.*

# Review your skills

## Check up

Review your response to the exam-style question on page 19. Tick ✓ the column to show how well you think you have done each of the following.

| | Had a go ✓ | Nearly there ✓ | Got it! ✓ |
|---|---|---|---|
| identified details in the source | ☐ | ☐ | ☐ |
| asked a valid question | ☐ | ☐ | ☐ |
| assessed the usefulness of follow-up sources. | ☐ | ☐ | ☐ |

## Need more practice?

If you want to practise another exam-style question, try ✎ this one on a separate piece of paper:

### Exam-style question

**Study Source A on page 19.**

How could you follow up Source A to find out more about the issues affecting children in Whitechapel in the 1880s?

In your answer, you must give the question you would ask and the type of source you could use.

Complete the table below.                                                  **(4 marks)**

Detail in Source A that I would follow up:

.............................................................................................................................

Question I would ask:

.............................................................................................................................

What type of source I could use:

.............................................................................................................................

How this might help answer my question:

.............................................................................................................................

How confident do you feel about each of these **skills**? Colour ✎ in the bars.

**1** How do I identify details in the source?

**2** How do I ask good questions about the source?

**3** How do I select valid methods of answering my question?

# ③ Source provenance, usefulness and reliability

This unit will help you to decide how useful a source is. The skills you will build are to:

- choose details from a source based on what is useful for investigating a given topic
- recognise the limitations of sources in finding out what you need to know
- make judgements about the provenance of a source to help your explanation.

In the exam, you will also be asked to tackle questions such as the one below. This unit will prepare you to write your own response to this question.

**Exam-style question**

Study Sources A and B on page 25.

How useful are Sources A and B for an enquiry into the difficulties the police faced in trying to capture the East End serial murderer?

Explain your answer, using Sources A and B and your knowledge of the historical context.   **(8 marks)**

As you read a source, ask yourself the following questions:

**?** Who made/wrote it?

**?** What details might not be useful?

**?** Why might it not be reliable?

**?** Why was it made/written?

**?** Is this type of source useful to me to answer my questions?

**?** What details might be useful?

The three key questions in the **skills boosts** will help you to analyse and evaluate a source to decide how useful it is.

**①** How do I identify what is useful to an historian?

**②** How do I identify the limitations of a source?

**③** How do I include judgements about the provenance of the source?

Look at the extract student response to the following exam-style question. It is a source utility question. This extract covers how useful the student thinks Source C is.

**Exam-style question**

How useful are Sources C and D for an enquiry into methods of investigation in Whitechapel in the late 19th century?

Explain your answer, using Sources C and D and your knowledge of the historical context.

**Source C** *The recollections of inspector Frederick Abberline, reported in the* Pall Mall Gazette, *24 March 1903.*

I gave myself up to the study of the cases. Many a time, even after we had carried our inquiries as far as we could – and we made no fewer than 1,600 sets of papers about our investigations – instead of going home when I was off duty, I used to patrol the district until four or five o'clock in the morning. While keeping my eyes wide open for clues of any kind, many and many a time I gave those wretched, homeless women, who were Jack the Ripper's special prey, fourpence or sixpence for a shelter to get them away from the streets and out of harm's way.

Source C is useful to an enquiry into policing techniques as it tells us about the police looking for clues to the Ripper investigation whilst 'on the beat'. It describes how hard the police were working to try and solve the case, working through paperwork and completing searches. During the case, the police received over 300 letters and postcards from men claiming to be the murderer, all leads that they then had to spend time following up. We can assume that as a police officer working the case he was fully aware of the amount of time individuals were putting into the investigation. However, his description is for an article being published in a newspaper so he may have wanted to create a sense of sympathy or support for the police by assuring the public they were doing their best to identify the murderer.

(1) Read the student response and then do the following:

a Highlight ✍ in one colour details about the source that they find useful.

b Highlight ✍ in another colour where they have discussed the limitations of the source.
   Fill in ✍ the colour code key to help you.

   **Colour code:** Useful source ☐    Source limitation ☐

c Circle Ⓐ any text using or questioning the impact of the provenance of the source.

d Underline A any text where the student has used their own knowledge to explain how the source is useful or its limitations.

# Improvements in policing

This unit uses the theme of improvements in policing to build your skills in assessing the usefulness of a source. If you need to review your knowledge of this theme, work through these pages.

**1** One new investigation technique employed by the police in Whitechapel was to keep photographic records of all suspects to be stored in a central file. These identifiers could then be used to catch repeat criminals. What were these photographic records commonly known as? Tick (✓) your choice.

Mug shots ☐      Head photos ☐      Forensics ☐

**2** **a** From the context of developing investigation techniques, describe (✎) the following terms:

    **i** Bertillon System ......................................................................................................................................

    **ii** Mug shots ...........................................................................................................................................

    **iii** Forensics ............................................................................................................................................

    **iv** Telephone boxes ................................................................................................................................

  **b** Write (✎) two criticisms of police techniques applied during the Ripper case in the Whitechapel investigations.

    1 ........................................................................................................................................................

    2 ........................................................................................................................................................

**3** Read the descriptions below.

| | | |
|---|---|---|
| By the end of the 19th century the Metropolitan Police were benefiting from the installation of telephone lines. | Using evidence from post mortems to gather clues as to the identity of the murderer (e.g. likely to be left-handed). | The Bertillon System. Taking photographic records and measurements of all suspects to keep on file. |
| Setting up soup kitchens to encourage witnesses to come forward. | Following up on journalists' theories. | Following up on clues found with the victims to establish their identity and possible connections to their murderer. |

  **a** Highlight (✎) in one colour those techniques used early in the investigation (after the discovery of Mary Ann Nichols' body on 31 August 1888).

  **b** Highlight (✎) in another colour those techniques developed as a result of lessons learned over the course of the investigation.

    Fill in (✎) the colour code key to help you.

    **Colour code:** Early in investigation ☐      After investigation ☐

**4** **a** Following the Ripper case some lessons were learned and improvements made to policing and the environment of Whitechapel. Draw ✐ lines linking the solutions to the problems they attempted to solve.

| A Poor communication | a The Working Classes Act (1890) and the Public Health Amendment Act (1890). |

| B Lack of forensic techniques | b 1901 a telephone line was installed in H Division HQ after success in Glasgow. |

| C The social environment of Whitechapel | c Increased size of the database of criminal mug shots and fingerprinting records. |

**b** Select one solution and explain ✐ how it improved the problem it is linked to.

........................................................................................................................................

........................................................................................................................................

**5** **a** Below are three new techniques used by the police force after 1900. Below each technique, write ✐ a brief description.

**b** Draw ✐ lines linking each technique to descriptions of how it might improve the effectiveness of police investigations after 1900. A technique may link to more than one description.

| A Bertillon System | a Increased communication between different police forces |
| ..................................... | |
| ..................................... | b Police divisions could share information about criminals |
| ..................................... | |

| B Improvements in the environment of Whitechapel | c People's attitudes about the link between crime and poverty changed and less emphasis was put on 'defects in the character of the poor' |
| ..................................... | |
| ..................................... | d Descriptions could be matched to a growing database of known criminals |
| ..................................... | |

| C Telephone lines to police stations | e Witnesses could use mug shots to identify who they saw |
| ..................................... | |
| ..................................... | f Authorities looked to make changes to the elements of the environment which were making policing more difficult – improving street lighting, for example |

# How do I identify what is useful to an historian?

To answer a source utility question, you need to identify the details the source is providing that are useful to an historian studying a particular topic, which will be identified in the question. To do this you should:

- identify the topic about crime and policing in Whitechapel that the question requires you to focus on
- select appropriate details from the source, which help you learn more about this topic.

**Source A** *Police letter, 9 October 1888. From Charles Warren to Sir James Fraser during the investigation into the Jack the Ripper Case.*

My dear Fraser,

In order to prevent our working doubly over the same ground I have to suggest that our CID should be in more constant communication with yours about the W[hitechapel] murders. Could you send an officer to Ch[ief] Insp[ector] Swanson here every morning to consult or may I send an officer every morning to consult with your officers.

We are inundated with suggestions and names of suspects.

Truly Yours,

C.W. [Charles Warren]

1. A good place to start is by asking: who, why, when, where, how? Consider the focus of the question and develop new questions using these stems. An historian has done this when investigating the difficulties the police faced in trying to capture the East End serial murderer:

> **?** What was the nature of the obstacles?

> **?** Did the police have any idea about why the murders were happening?

> **?** What techniques were the police using?

> **?** Who within the police were involved in the investigation?

Circle Ⓐ the text in Source A and draw ✏ a line linking it to the questions in the thought bubbles above.

2. Look at Source B. Circle Ⓐ the text and draw ✏ a line linking it to the questions in the thought bubbles above.

**Source B** *From the coroner's report of Dr Wynne Baxter into the murder of Annie Chapman, 14 September 1888.*

The injuries had been made by someone who had considerable anatomical skill and knowledge. There were no meaningless cuts. The organ [Chapman's womb] had been taken by one who knew where to find it. No unskilled person could have known this or have recognised it when found. For instance, no mere slaughterer of animals could have carried out these operations. It must have been someone accustomed to the post mortem room with a desire to possess the missing organ.

**How do I identify the limitations of a source?**

When identifying how useful a source is, you must always remember to consider the possible limitations in content and its reliability. Remember, as well as how much relevant information it contains, you will need to think about:

- who created the source and their reasons for creating it – this is the source's **provenance** and it can tell you about how reliable the source is
- how typical you think the information given in the source is.

To find what the limitations of a source are and how useful it is, you need to study the provenance of the source – the **N**ature, **O**rigin and **P**urpose (NOP).

| Nature | Origin | Purpose |
|---|---|---|
| **What** kind of source is it? A photo, a diary, an official record? This is the **nature** of the source. | **Who** created it and **when**? Did they witness the events first-hand? Are they having to remember events? This is the **origin** of the source. | **Why** was the source created? For a photograph: is it natural or posed? Why did the photographer pick those people or that shot? For a written account: why was it written? To entertain, to persuade someone, to reassure someone? Who was meant to read it? This is the **purpose** of the source. |

(1) (a) Add notes on the provenance of Sources A and B from page 25 in the table below. The answer to some questions might be that you don't know.

| | Source A | Source B |
|---|---|---|
| Who created the source? | | |
| When did they create the source? | | |
| Did they witness the events first hand? | | |
| Why did they create the source? | | |

(b) Do you think Source A or B is the most reliable for answering an enquiry into the difficulties the police faced in trying to capture the East End serial murderer?

(2) Does the information in Source A agree with what you already know about the difficulties the police faced in trying to capture the East End serial murderer, or is it surprising? Explain your answer.

..............................................................................................................................................................

..............................................................................................................................................................

..............................................................................................................................................................

Some information in the source may contradict your own knowledge of a topic. Why might that be? Does it make the source less reliable?

## 3 How do I include judgements about the provenance of the source?

Once you have identified the useful aspects of the source and its limitations, you need to think about the provenance (nature, origin or purpose). How will these aspects affect how you use the source? You may feel a source is unreliable, but this does not mean it is useless; you need to make a judgement. You should always consider:

- What kind of source it is?
- Do the NOP provide detail that explains any differences between your own knowledge and the source content?

1 Consider Sources A and B from page 25 comparatively by completing the table below. Use the questions in the thought bubbles to help you. ✎

| | How do the NOP of the source provenance add strength to the usefulness of the source content? | How do the NOP of the source provenance weaken the usefulness of the source content? |
|---|---|---|
| Source A | | |
| Source B | | |

? Why might a letter by Charles Warren from 1888 be more likely to include accurate details about difficulties in policing?

? Does the fact it was written by Charles Warren for the identified purpose raise questions about accuracy in regard to difficulties facing the police?

? Why might a coroners report about one of the victims from 1888 be more likely to include accurate details about difficulties in policing?

? Does the fact it is a coroners report raise questions about accuracy in regard to difficulties facing the police?

2 Choose one of the sources. Complete ✎ the following sentences to reach a judgement on how useful the source would be to an enquiry about the difficulties the police faced in trying to capture the East End murderer.

Give an example of something about the provenance you feel makes the source less reliable.

Try to explain how this might affect how you would use it.

a An historian should treat Source ........ with caution because

..................................................................................................

..................................................................................................

..................................................................................................

Give an example of something about the provenance you feel makes the source more reliable.

b The provenance of this source makes it useful because ................

..................................................................................................

Try to explain how this might affect how you would use it.

..................................................................................................

# Sample response

Read through the student's response to this exam-style question. Sources A and B are on page 25.

**Exam-style question**

How useful are Sources A and B for an enquiry into the difficulties the police faced in trying to capture the East End serial murderer? Explain your answer, using Sources A and B and your knowledge of the historical context.

---

Source A is useful to an enquiry into the difficulties the police faced in trying to capture the East End serial murderer because it implies that the police and the CID were not communicating well enough. It also implies that this might be improved by sending an officer each morning to consult with the CID. The CID team had been assigned to the Jack the Ripper case to assist the uniformed police with their enquiries, but as a result of the lack of communication following leads and detecting suspects were inefficient.

Source B is from the coroner's report of Dr Wynne Baxter into the murder of Annie Chapman, so it is useful in showing us how the police were able to follow up the clues as a result of the post mortems. The report suggests the killer was left-handed and knew about anatomy.

A letter written in Source A in October 1888 is by Charles Warren who was Police Commissioner and therefore he had first-hand experience of communications between uniformed police and the CID. He might also be emphasising the efforts that the police force in Whitechapel were making in order to improve communications.

Identifies content that is useful from Source A ☐

Identifies content that is useful from Source B ☐

Identifies an element of provenance that may be useful ☐

Identifies an element of provenance that may limit how the source is used ☐

① Read the key features of an effective answer next to the student answer. Tick ⊘ the ones you feel the student has achieved.

② Draw ✎ arrows from each ticked box and circle Ⓐ the relevant passages in the answer to show that key feature.

③ What would you add to the student's answer in order to achieve all four key features? ✎

.........................................................................................................................

.........................................................................................................................

.........................................................................................................................

.........................................................................................................................

# Your turn!

Now try this exam-style question using the prompts in the student plan to help you plan your answer. Plan and write ✏ your answer on a separate piece of paper.

**Exam-style question**

How useful are Sources C and D for an enquiry into investigative techniques in the late 19th century? Explain your answer, using Sources C and D and your knowledge of the historical context.

**Source C** | *The recollections of inspector Frederick Abberline, reported in the* Pall Mall Gazette, *24 March 1903.*

I gave myself up to the study of the cases. Many a time, even after we had carried our inquiries as far as we could – and we made no fewer than 1,600 sets of papers about our investigations – instead of going home when I was off duty, I used to patrol the district until four or five o'clock in the morning. While keeping my eyes wide open for clues of any kind, many and many a time I gave those wretched, homeless women, who were Jack the Ripper's special prey, fourpence or sixpence for a shelter to get them away from the streets and out of harm's way.

**Source D** | *The Bertillon method of criminal identification, developed by the French criminologist, Alphonse Bertillon, was used by London police from 1894. The image shows men filing criminal records, notably full face photographs and profiles and body measurements, following the Bertillon method, Paris 1910–1915.*

|  | Source C | Source D |
|---|---|---|
| **Content strengths** What I have found out about investigative techniques in the late 19th century from the sources | | |
| **Knowledge check** Does my own knowledge suggest this is accurate? | | |
| **Provenance** | Nature: Origin: Purpose: | Nature: Origin: Purpose: |
| **Most useful element of provenance** | | |
| **Biggest limitation of provenance** | | |

# Review your skills

## Check up

Review your response to the exam-style question on page 29. Tick ✓ the column to show how well you think you have done each of the following.

| | Had a go ✓ | Nearly there ✓ | Got it! ✓ |
|---|---|---|---|
| identified the aspects of content that are useful to an historian studying investigative techniques in the late 19th century (utility) | ☐ | ☐ | ☐ |
| identified elements of the provenance of the source (nature, origin, purpose) which make the source more useful (utility) | ☐ | ☐ | ☐ |
| identified accuracy of the provenance of the source (nature, origin, purpose) which means the source must be used with caution (limitations) | ☐ | ☐ | ☐ |

## Need more practice?

If you want to practise another 8-mark question, try this one 🖉 on a separate piece of paper.

### Exam-style question

Study Sources A and B on page 25.

How useful are Sources A and B for an enquiry into the improvements in policing during the Whitechapel murders?

Explain your answer, using Sources A and B and your knowledge of the historical context.     (8 marks)

How confident do you feel about each of these **skills**? Colour 🖉 in the bars.

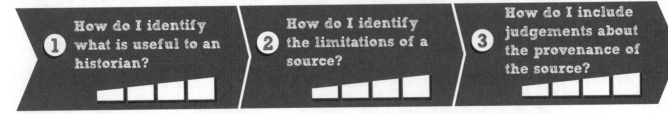

1 How do I identify what is useful to an historian?

2 How do I identify the limitations of a source?

3 How do I include judgements about the provenance of the source?

# ④ Answering relevantly

This unit will help you to learn how you can answer a question as relevantly as possible. The skills you will build are to:

- recognise the demands of the question
- stick to the focus of the question
- plan a relevant answer to the question.

In the exam, you will be asked to tackle a question such as the one below. This unit will prepare you to write your own response to this exam-style question.

**Exam-style question**

Explain **one** way in which types of crime in Anglo-Saxon Britain were the same as types of crime in Norman Britain.

(4 marks)

The three key questions in the **skills boosts** will help you to recognise the demands of the question and ensure that you answer relevantly.

 **How do I read the question?**

 **How do I identify relevant detail?**

 **How do I plan my answer to ensure it answers the question?**

Turn over to see one student's response to a similar exam-style question.

Look at this exam-style question:

**Exam-style question**

Explain **one** way in which law enforcement in Anglo-Saxon Britain was the same as law enforcement in Norman Britain.

(4 marks)

(1) Highlight (✏️) what you think are the most important parts of this exam-style question.

Read this extract from a student answer for this exam-style question.

> During Norman rule people continued to use hue and cry to enforce the law and track down possible criminals. This continued the law enforcement from the Anglo-Saxon period, when witnesses within the community were expected to alert the rest of their community when they saw a crime taking place so that the criminal could be caught and punished. This fitted in with the fact that people continued to live in small communities so law enforcement run by the community continued to make sense. In Norman law if the community in which the crime took place failed to capture the accused, that community would be responsible for a fine... – Murdrum fine – was paid to the king's officials.

(2) Circle (Ⓐ) the sections of the answer that are about aspects staying the same.

(3) Underline (Ⓐ) the sections of the answer that are about change.

(4) Look at your selections. Highlight (✏️) those that you think are most relevant to the question.

Judgement about the relevance of content should be based on three elements identified in the question:
- time parameter
- topic
- comparison focus (e.g. change or continuity).

Here, the elements would be:
- Anglo-Saxon and Norman periods
- law enforcement
- law enforcement that is the same in both periods.

# Anglo-Saxon and Norman crime and punishment

This unit uses the theme of Anglo-Saxon and Norman crime and punishment to build your skills in answering relevantly. If you need to review your knowledge of this theme, work through these pages.

**1** Read the passage below about the changes the Normans made to crime and punishment (c1000–1200). Underline Ⓐ the most appropriate words in bold to complete the description.

> The desire to be more powerful **motivated/impeded** Norman kings to make punishments **harsher/less harsh**. For example, there was an increase in the number of crimes punishable by death or mutilation. This also applied to new laws and under the new Forest Laws **poaching/slander** was punishable by death. Norman kings also increased their control over law and order by making all fines payable to the **king's officials/victim's family**. The Normans, however, **continued/changed** to use the hue and cry system to catch criminals as it **prevented/encouraged** villagers avoiding responsibility for law and order. The Norman system of law was based on the idea that all men should be safe from crime under the king's authority. This was called the king's Mund and it was a crime to disrupt this peace, much as it was in Anglo-Saxon law.

**2** Draw 🖉 lines linking the headings on the left to the descriptions of the crimes and law enforcement strategies on the right.

| | |
|---|---|
| A Shire reeve | **a** Crimes like assault or murder that cause physical harm to another person |
| B Crimes against the person | **b** Crimes like theft, robbery and arson that involve taking or damaging property that does not belong to you |
| C Moral crimes | **c** Being held responsible for the actions of the other members of your community. For example, in a village community if one person committed a crime everyone else would have to take action |
| D Hue and cry | **d** Actions which don't match up to society's view of decent behaviour. For example, sex outside of marriage or breaking from rules and customs of the Church |
| E Collective responsibility | **e** Local man appointed to bring criminals to justice |
| F Crimes against property | **f** Literally shouting for help. The responsibility of anyone who witnessed a crime |

In the table below there are some new Norman ideas hidden among the Anglo-Saxon approaches to crime and punishment.

**(3) a** Circle Ⓐ the ideas which were introduced by the Normans.

**b** Highlight ✏ the crimes associated with the person, property and authority in three different colours. This will help you to see what the new ideas were mainly about. Fill in ✏ the colour code key to help you.

**Colour code:** Person ☐     Property ☐     Authority ☐

| | | |
|---|---|---|
| Theft | Arson | Disrupting the king's peace |
| Hue and cry | Murder | Murdrum fines payable to the king's officials |
| Wergild payments to the victim's family | Poaching | Disrupting the king's Mund |

**(4)** Using the information in the table above, list ✏ the new ideas that you have circled under the correct factor of influence.

| Factor of influence | Example of new idea |
|---|---|
| King wants more control of law and order | |
| The introduction of the feudal system | |
| King wants to protect Normans against the Saxons | |
| King wants exclusive hunting rights | |

**How do I read the question?**

To identify the focus so you can answer the exam question relevantly you need to:
- look at the time period(s) mentioned – the **time parameter**
- identify the **topic/theme** the question is asking you to focus on
- make **comparisons** to determine how much things changed or stayed the same.

The exam question will cover **time parameters** or time periods.

(1) Look at the exam-style question below and circle (A) the **time parameters**.

> **Exam-style question**
>
> Explain **one** way in which types of crime in Anglo-Saxon Britain were similar to types of crime in Norman Britain.                                                      **(4 marks)**

(2) The question will also ask you to focus on one of the **topics/common themes** you have studied in the Crime and Punishment thematic study, such as:

(?) the nature of crimes

(?) how criminals were punished

(?) how the law was enforced

(?) which factors influenced crime and punishment, e.g. key individuals, attitudes in society, religion, etc...

Look at the exam-style question below and underline (A) the **topic/theme**.

> **Exam-style question**
>
> Explain **one** way in which punishments in Anglo-Saxon Britain were different from punishments in Norman Britain.                                                      **(4 marks)**

Finally, you need to identify what **comparisons** the question is asking you to make, whether things are similar or different between the two time periods and how. Answering how things were the same/ different is key to explaining.

(3) Look at the exam-style question below and highlight (✎) the **comparison focus**.

> **Exam-style question**
>
> Explain **one** way in which types of crime in Anglo-Saxon Britain were different from types of crime in Norman Britain.                                                      **(4 marks)**

To be relevant your answer must stick to the time period(s), topic and comparison focus identified in the question. Anything outside of this could be considered irrelevant.

(4) Look again at the three exam-style questions on this page and, where you haven't already, circle (A) the time parameter, underline (A) the topic/theme and highlight (✎) the comparison focus for each one.

# 2 How do I identify relevant detail?

To develop your answer it is necessary to support the focus you have identified in the question with relevant details from your own knowledge.

(1) Look at the exam-style question below. Circle Ⓐ the time parameters, underline Ⓐ the topic/theme focus and highlight 🖉 the comparison focus.

**Exam-style question**

Explain **one** way in which law enforcement in Anglo-Saxon Britain was different from law enforcement in Norman Britain.

(4 marks)

(2) Do the same as you have done in (1) for the student's notes. Summarise your findings in the table below, by placing a tick ✓ or cross ✗ in each cell.

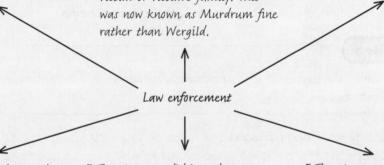

A During Norman rule people continued to use hue and cry to enforce the law and deliver a suspect to justice. This involved any witnesses of crime shouting out to alert the rest of the community in order to catch the suspect.

B As the Norman Kings wanted to fully establish their control over England they changed law enforcement so that fines from failure to comply with hue and cry were paid to their officials rather than by the accused to... to the victim or victim's family. This was now known as Murdrum fine rather than Wergild.

C During the Anglo-Saxon period, a suspect they would be charged a fine, to be paid to the victim or victim's family as a form of compensation. How much you paid depended on the social status of the victim.

Law enforcement

D Once a suspect was delivered to justice, God would be the final judge of whether they were guilty or innocent. The accused would receive a trial by ordeal through which God could give a sign of his verdict. Trial by ordeal continued to be used during Norman rule.

E The Normans did introduce an additional trial by ordeal — trial by combat. This was often used by the Normans to settle disputes over large sums of money or land, so between the nobility. The method was to allow the two people involved in the dispute to fight using large sticks or swords.

F The Normans took ownership of what had previously been common land. On the common land people had been able to graze their animals and catch rabbits. Once it was under the strict control of the king it became illegal to hunt on it. Some people continued to hunt to supplement their food and this was now treated as a crime called poaching.

|  | A | B | C | D | E | F |
|---|---|---|---|---|---|---|
| Time parameter |  |  |  |  |  |  |
| Topic |  |  |  |  |  |  |
| Comparison focus |  |  |  |  |  |  |

For these 4-mark questions, you only need to talk about **one** way in which things changed or stayed the same.

## 3 How do I plan my answer to ensure it answers the question?

As well as selecting relevant content knowledge to support your answer, it is important that you explain how there was a similarity or a difference.

Look at the following exam-style question and the example student answer below it.

### Exam-style question

Explain **one** way in which punishments in Anglo-Saxon Britain were different from punishments in Norman Britain.

(4 marks)

One way in which punishments in Anglo-Saxon Britain were different from punishments in Norman Britain is that fines were charged to the community for failure to bring a suspect to justice and were paid to the king's officials. This differed to Anglo Saxon fines which were charged to the suspect and paid to the victim or victim's family. During the Anglo-Saxon period these fines had been a form of compensation for the victim's loss.

One way to make sure your answer answers the question is to use the following checklist.

| Checklist<br>Have I: | ✓ |
|---|---|
| identified one difference? | |
| selected content knowledge for that difference for the first time period required? | |
| selected content knowledge for that difference for the second time period required? | |
| explained how there is a similarity or a difference? | |

**1** Tick ✓ the checklist to decide if everything necessary has been covered in the sample student answer.

You can use specific language to make it clear that you have identified whether there is a similarity or a difference. Here are some words and phrases that will help you to do this.

| still | remained | continued | however |
| persisted | also | changed | but |
| was now | in contrast | are different | whereas |

**2** Read through the sample student answer above and highlight 🖉 where they have used words to show similarity or difference.

**3** Have a go at rewriting 🖉 the answer above to include more of the phrases from the word box.

.......................................................................................

.......................................................................................

.......................................................................................

.......................................................................................

.......................................................................................

.......................................................................................

# Sample response

Read through the student's response to the following exam-style question.

**Exam-style question**

Explain **one** way in which punishments in Anglo-Saxon Britain were the same as punishments in Norman Britain.

(4 marks)

*During the Anglo-Saxon period mutilation and the death penalty were common punishments for those found guilty of a crime. The Normans continued to apply these punishments although there were an increased number of crimes that were punishable by death, such as the new Forest Laws and in particular poaching. Mutilation continued to take the form of branding or chopping off a body part as this ensured the community could identify the person as a criminal.*

(1) Complete ✏ the details below to decide upon the focus of the exam-style question.

Time period: ....................................................................................................................................

Topic/theme: ....................................................................................................................................

Comparison focus: ....................................................................................................................................

(2) Highlight ✏ the sections of the student's answer you think are most relevant to the focus of this question.

(3) **a** Cross out (cat) any sections that are not relevant to the question and therefore unnecessary for the student to include in their answer.

**b** Why are these sections irrelevant? (Think about the focus you identified.) ✏

....................................................................................................................................

....................................................................................................................................

(4) Consider the student's answer above and tick ✓ the following checklist:

| Checklist | |
|---|---|
| Has the student: | ✓ |
| identified one similarity? | |
| selected content knowledge for that similarity for the first time period required? | |
| selected content knowledge for that similarity for the second time period required? | |
| explained how there is a similarity or difference? | |

(5) Highlight ✏ the student's answer where they have used words to show similarity or difference.

# Your turn!

Now try this exam-style question using the prompts below.

**Exam-style question**

Explain **one** way in which the role of the community in Anglo-Saxon Britain was similar to the role of the community in Norman Britain. **(4 marks)**

**(1)** In the exam-style question:

   **a** circle Ⓐ the time parameters

   **b** underline Ⓐ the topic/theme focus

   **c** highlight 🖉 the comparison focus.

**(2)** List 🖉 four pieces of content knowledge relevant to the question. Include as much detail as possible.

........................................................   ........................................................

........................................................   ........................................................

........................................................   ........................................................

........................................................   ........................................................

**(3) a** Consider your notes above and tick ✓ if they meet the criteria in the checklist:

| Checklist | ✓ |
|---|---|
| Is it relevant to the Anglo-Saxon and Norman periods? | |
| Is it relevant to the role of the community? | |
| Does it identify a similarity between the periods? | |

   **b** Look at your notes above and highlight 🖉 the content knowledge that most clearly shows one difference between the time periods.

**(4)** Write 🖉 a brief bullet point plan of your answer.

**(5)** Now write 🖉 your response to the question on a separate piece of paper. As you write, think carefully about:

- the relevance of the details you are using
- explaining the comparison between the two periods clearly.

**Unit 4 Answering relevantly**    **39**

# Review your skills

## Check up

Review your response to the exam-style question on page 39. Tick ✓ the column to show how well you think you have done each of the following.

|  | Had a go ✓ | Nearly there ✓ | Got it! ✓ |
|---|---|---|---|
| identified the time parameters of the question | ☐ | ☐ | ☐ |
| identified the topic or theme focus | ☐ | ☐ | ☐ |
| selected content knowledge that was relevant to the question | ☐ | ☐ | ☐ |
| compared the situation between the two periods clearly | ☐ | ☐ | ☐ |

## Need more practice?

You will need to practise what has been covered in this unit to answer other exam-style questions in this workbook. If you want to practise another 4-mark similarity and difference question, try ✐ this one on a separate piece of paper:

**Exam-style question**

Explain **one** way in which the role of the community in Anglo-Saxon Britain was different from the role of the community in Norman Britain.

(4 marks)

How confident do you feel about each of these **skills**? Colour ✐ in the bars.

**1** How do I read the question?

**2** How do I identify relevant detail?

**3** How do I plan my answer to ensure it answers the question?

# ⑤ Selecting and using supporting evidence

This unit will help you to select and deploy relevant supporting evidence from your content knowledge in your answers.

The skills you will build are to:

- select information relevant to the question
- ensure that the evidence selected is the most relevant to the concept (i.e. change or causes)
- move beyond the suggested content and include relevant ideas of your own.

In the exam, you will be asked to tackle a question such as the one below. This unit will prepare you to write your own response to this exam-style question.

The three key questions in the **skills boosts** will help you to select and deploy supporting evidence.

 **1** How do I select information to answer the question?

 **2** How do I ensure that information is relevant to the concept focus?

 **3** How do I use information of my own?

Look at the following exam-style question and the student plan beneath it.

**Exam-style question**

Explain why there were changes in law enforcement in the period 1900 to the present.

You may use the following in your answer:

- specialist police units
- CCTV.

You **must** also use information of your own.

(12 marks)

Paragraph 1: specialist police units

- As the stock market grew during the 20th century there was a need to build in protection from criminal activity. As a result, a specialist fraud squad was set up and trained to have specialist financial and business knowledge, making investigations and detection more effective.

- As travel has become easier people have started to traffic more and more drugs. By creating a specialist drugs unit police have the expertise to use intelligence to disrupt drugs deals and trafficking before the drugs reach the general public. This in turn can reduce drug-related crimes.

Paragraph 2: CCTV

- Advances in video technology during the 20th century have made it possible to take large amounts of video footage of the general public and monitor Britain's streets.

- This is based on the continued belief that if a person knows they can be identified it will deter them from committing a crime. This is the same belief that hue and cry and the beat constable were based on.

(1) Highlight 🖉 the ideas in the plan which are relevant to the question.

Think about:
- the focus of the question – law enforcement
- the time period (1900 to the present)
- the concept – causation. Why was there change?

(2) From your own knowledge, write 🖉 three other ideas that would also be relevant to the three criteria in the question.

1 ........................................................................................................................................

........................................................................................................................................

........................................................................................................................................

2 ........................................................................................................................................

........................................................................................................................................

........................................................................................................................................

3 ........................................................................................................................................

........................................................................................................................................

........................................................................................................................................

# Change and continuity in crime and punishment from 1900 to the present

This unit uses the theme of change and continuity in crime and punishment from 1900 to the present to build your skills in selecting and using supporting evidence. If you need to review your knowledge of this theme, work through these pages.

Look at the modern methods of dealing with crime listed below.

**1** **a** Highlight 🖉 the methods of **preventing** a crime.

**b** Circle Ⓐ the methods of **solving** a crime.

| | |
|---|---|
| **Breathalysers** (1967) – allow police to test blood alcohol level immediately at the roadside – and **speed cameras** (1992). | **Closed circuit television (CCTV)** films people's movements in public areas. |
| **Improved communications** – a wider range of records are kept, which can be accessed at scene using new technologies like tablets and smartphones. | Increases in **data management** – for example, the DNA database, which in 2015 held the profiles of 5.7 million individuals. |
| Improvements in **forensic sciences** – forensic teams carry out detailed searches at crime scenes looking for decisive evidence such as DNA and fingerprints. | **Biometric screening** – records unique characteristics such as fingerprints or eye patterns to restrict access to owners and those with permissions. |
| **Mass video surveillance** – allows private companies and authorities to analyse large amounts of online behaviour to predict acts of terrorism and other criminal activity. | **Improved computer software** – can analyse large amounts of video footage very quickly to identify criminals. |

**2** **a** Circle Ⓐ the statement below that you think best describes the methods of dealing with crime in the 20th century. Consider the significance of the methods, not just the number of them.

| Predominantly to prevent | Predominantly to solve | An even mix |
|---|---|---|

**b** Explain 🖉 why you made this decision.

..............................................................................................................................................

..............................................................................................................................................

..............................................................................................................................................

..............................................................................................................................................

(3) Over the last 200 years attitudes have changed and society puts a lot more emphasis on rehabilitating criminals. Modern courts often use alternative punishments to prison. Classify each of the alternatives by colouring (✏) in the box beside each heading, to show which of the following categories it fits. To help you, fill in (✏) the colour code key below.

**Colour code:** Control actions ☐     Reform ☐     Keep community safe ☐

(4) Under each description, explain (✏) why they might reform the person convicted of the crime.

| Anti-social behaviour order | Community service | Restorative justice |
|---|---|---|
| A court order to restrict what a person can do and with whom they can have contact. | A court order to do supervised work that benefits the community. | A supervised meeting between the criminal and the victim (or victim's relatives) to discuss the crime and to help understand the impact of their actions. |
| **Drug and alcohol treatment programmes** | **Electronic tagging** | **Care orders** |
| For crimes committed as a result of drug or alcohol dependency, help and treatment is offered to overcome addiction. | The tag strictly controls where the wearer can go and when they can leave their house. | Usually put on young offenders to support them to make the right choices, rather than sending them to prison. |

(5) Look at the 20th-century prison reforms on the timeline below. Highlight (✏) which you think had the most significant impact on rehabilitating prisoners.

| | |
|---|---|
| 1896 | Mentally ill prisoners treated separately to other prisoners |
| 1902 | Hard labour in prisons ended |
| 1907 | Probation officers employed to monitor offenders living outside of prison |
| 1922 | Increased focus on prisoner welfare. Separate system abolished and education opportunities introduced |
| 1933 | New focus on preparing prisoners for life after serving their sentence. Open prisons and day-release |
| 1963 and 1969 | Youth justice reforms. Raised the age of responsibility to 10 years and encouraged alternatives to prison |

**How do I select information to answer the question?**

In these questions you must use your own content knowledge, but selection must be relevant to the question.

Look again at this exam-style question:

**Exam-style question**

Explain why there were changes in law enforcement in the period 1900 to the present.

You may use the following in your answer:

• specialist police units

• closed circuit TV (CCTV).

You **must** also use information of your own.

(12 marks)

**(1)**  **a**  Circle Ⓐ the focus topic/theme.

**b**  Highlight 🖉 the time period.

**c**  Underline Ⓐ the concept. What is the question asking you to do?

**(2)**  Look at the spider diagram of content knowledge below.

**a**  Cross out ꞁꞁꞁ any content knowledge that does not fit the topic/theme focus.

**b**  Cross out ꞁꞁꞁ any content knowledge that does not fit the time parameters.

**c**  Cross out ꞁꞁꞁ any content knowledge that does not fit the concept.

**d**  Write 🖉 what content knowledge you are left with.

These indicators will help you to select relevant evidence from your own knowledge.

...................................................................................................

...................................................................................................

Everything you are left with should be relevant to the question, and can be used as supporting evidence in your answer.

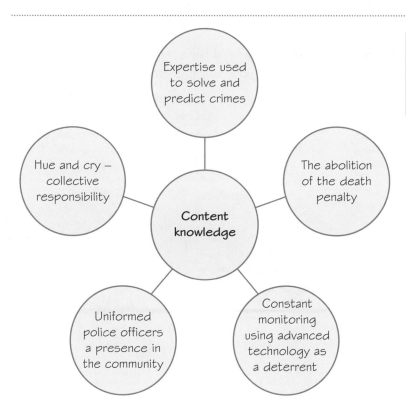

## 2 How do I ensure that information is relevant to the concept focus?

Each 'Explain why...' question will ask you to explain why something either changed or stayed the same. It is important to identify which it is asking for and explain how your supporting evidence explains this. The exam-style question on page 45 is asking you to explain why there was **change**.

**1 a** The exam-style question on page 45 suggests you may use 'specialist police units' and 'CCTV' in your answer. Read the student answer below and underline (A) the reason(s) they give for specialist police units leading to a period of change in law enforcement in the period 1900 to the present.

> As a result of increased movement around the globe, crimes such as drug trafficking have increased in the period 1900 to the present. In order to detect and prevent these crimes the police have created specialist units, who can use their expert training to identify and disrupt trade before the drugs reach the public. To do this effectively they are now able to use new surveillance technologies to monitor the actions of suspects and forecast crimes. Law enforcement has changed as a result of the nature of crime changing. It has been made more effective by the use of new technologies.

**b** Circle (A) which of the following best summarise(s) the reason(s) you have identified.

| Better transportation. | The availability of new technology. | Specialist crimes require specialist skills to detect them effectively. |

A **change** is when things become very different to how they were before.
A **continuity** is when things stay the same or very similar for a period of time.
This question requires you to focus on the **change**, so why things were different.

**2** Describe one way 'specialist police units' have changed law enforcement using your own knowledge to complete the flow diagram. Remember your examples must both be from the period 1900 to the present.

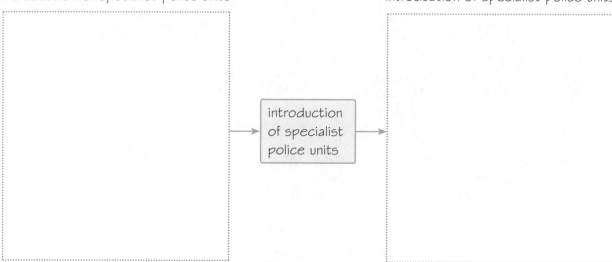

Law enforcement technique before the introduction of specialist police units

introduction of specialist police units

Law enforcement technique after the introduction of specialist police units

**How do I use information of my own?**

To move beyond the ideas given in the question you will need to write a third paragraph that, while still relevant to the topic focus, time parameters and concept, is not related to the two bullet-pointed prompts.

The bullet-pointed prompts in the exam-style question on page 45 are 'specialist police units' and 'CCTV'.

The table below includes ideas to answer this question. All are relevant to change in law enforcement in the period 1900 to the present.

| Developments in forensic science such as DNA profiling. | The fingerprinting branch of the Metropolitan Police set up in 1901. | Improvements in microscopes. |
|---|---|---|
| Improved / instant communication methods and large databases of information help police forces to share and communicate. | The Police Training College – emphasis on training new recruits rather than learning on the job. | Improved computer software. |
| Mass surveillance techniques. | | Fraud squad set up in 1946 to protect and deal with the growing crime in business and the stock market. |

(1) Cross out (~~cat~~) any ideas that are related to 'specialist crime units' and 'CCTV'.

(2) Select one of the ideas you have left and use this to plan (✐) a third paragraph in the table below.

| Third point | |
|---|---|
| Supporting detail (from own knowledge) | |
| Explain the change this made | • Situation before change:  <br><br> • Change made:  <br><br> • Situation after change: |

# Sample response

Read through the student's response to this exam-style question.

**Exam-style question**

Explain why there were changes in law enforcement in the period 1900 to the present.

You may use the following in your answer:

- specialist police units

- CCTV.

You **must** also use information of your own. (12 marks)

As a result of increased movement around the globe, crimes such as drug trafficking have increased in the period 1900 to the present. In 1971 the Misuse of Drugs Act was passed making the misuse of a number of substances a criminal offence. In order to detect and prevent these crimes the police have created specialist units, which can use their expert training to identify and disrupt trade before the drugs reach the public. People convicted of dealing drugs can face a prison sentence. A similar specialist unit was also created during the 20th century to protect the growing stock market from associated financial and business crimes.

For these specialist units to operate effectively they are now able to use new surveillance technologies to monitor the actions of suspects and forecast crimes. One such surveillance technology – CCTV – monitors the behaviour of individuals so suspect behaviour is recorded and those involved identified. In the 19th century, the beat constable would be responsible for ensuring law and order on the streets by being a uniformed presence among the community. Law enforcement has changed as a result of the nature of crime changing, and it is made more effective by the use of new technologies.

Law enforcement has also been changed and made more effective by the ability to identify an individual's DNA. DNA profiles were first discovered in the 1950s but in 1988 the first murder conviction was made on the basis of DNA evidence taken from tiny quantities of hair, skin or bodily fluids found at the crime scene.

1 In the student response above:

a Highlight ✐ evidence that is relevant to the topic/theme focus of **changes in law enforcement.**

b Underline Ⓐ evidence that is **not** relevant to the time period **1900 to the present.**

c Circle Ⓐ evidence that is an attempt to explain how this **caused** change in law enforcement.

d Using the structure below, show how the student has used the evidence to explain how this led to a change in law enforcement. ✐

- Situation before change: ...............................................................................................................................

- Change made: ...............................................................................................................................................

- Situation after change: .................................................................................................................................

# Your turn!

Now try this exam-style question using the prompts below.

Explain why there were changes in criminal activity in the period 1900 to the present.

You may use the following in your answer:

- transport

- the internet.

You **must** also use information of your own.

(12 marks)

(1) First, identify the indicators in the exam-style question that will ensure your selection of supporting evidence is relevant. 🖉

Topic/theme focus: ..........................................................................................................................

Time parameters: ............................................................................................................................

Concept: ...........................................................................................................................................

(2) On a separate piece of paper, create 🖉 a spider diagram of relevant knowledge. Remember to include the two bullet-pointed ideas from the exam-style question as well as at least one other.

(3) Plan 🖉 your answer using the template below.

Relevant idea 1: .............................................................................................................................

Supporting evidence – details from content knowledge:

....................................................................................................................................................

....................................................................................................................................................

Explanation of how this detail led to changes – answers the question:

....................................................................................................................................................

....................................................................................................................................................

....................................................................................................................................................

Relevant idea 2: .............................................................................................................................

Supporting evidence – details from content knowledge:

....................................................................................................................................................

....................................................................................................................................................

Explanation of how this detail led to changes – answers the question:

....................................................................................................................................................

....................................................................................................................................................

....................................................................................................................................................

Relevant idea 3: .............................................................................................................................

Supporting evidence – details from content knowledge:

....................................................................................................................................................

....................................................................................................................................................

Explanation of how this detail led to changes – answers the question:

....................................................................................................................................................

....................................................................................................................................................

....................................................................................................................................................

# Review your skills

## Check up

Review your response to the exam-style question on page 49. Tick ✓ the column to show how well you think you have done each of the following.

| | Had a go ✓ | Nearly there ✓ | Got it! ✓ |
|---|:---:|:---:|:---:|
| used supporting evidence relevant to the topic/theme | ☐ | ☐ | ☐ |
| used supporting evidence relevant to the time period | ☐ | ☐ | ☐ |
| used supporting detail relevant to the concept | ☐ | ☐ | ☐ |
| used supporting evidence that goes beyond the two prompts provided | ☐ | ☐ | ☐ |

## Need more practice?

You will need to practise what has been covered in this unit to answer other exam-style questions in this workbook. If you want to practise another 12-mark question, try 🖉 this one on a separate piece of paper:

**Exam-style question**

Explain why punishments have changed during the period 1900 to the present.

You may use the following in your answer:

- death penalty
- rehabilitation.

You **must** also use information of your own. (12 marks)

How confident do you feel about each of these **skills**? Colour 🖉 in the bars.

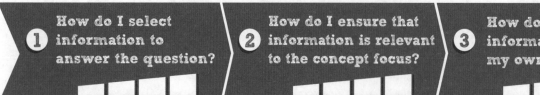

**1** How do I select information to answer the question?

**2** How do I ensure that information is relevant to the concept focus?

**3** How do I use information of my own?

# 6 Understanding change

This unit will help you to understand how historians identify and study change. Change is happening all the time. The skills you will build are to:

- identify changes that are historically significant
- describe this significance in your answers.

In the exam, you will be asked to tackle questions such as the one below. This unit will prepare you to write your own response to the following exam-style question. These questions are worth 16 marks – plus 4 marks for SPaG and specialist terminology.

## Exam-style question

'There was significant change in the nature of law enforcement in the period 1500–1700.'
How far do you agree? Explain your answer.

You may use the following in your answer:

- town constables
- hue and cry.

You **must** also use information of your own.

(16 marks) + (4 marks)

The three key questions in the **skills boosts** will help you to identify and describe historically significant change in a period.

 **1** How do I know what makes a change historically significant?

 **2** How do I distinguish between change and continuity?

 **3** How do I decide how significant a change is?

Look at the student's plan below for an answer to the exam-style question on page 51. Notice that they plan to give:

- two arguments to support the statement
- one argument against the statement.

They have also included the two suggested ideas from the exam-style question and one of their own.

---

**Paragraph 1:**
<u>Point</u>: Significant change in law enforcement as the role of the town constable changed.
<u>Evidence (supporting own knowledge)</u>: Town constables had already been introduced but their role was expanded to meet increased demand as crime rates went up. Larger populations led to an increase in monitoring and control, so new systems became necessary. People who had the money would appoint their own personal guard to protect their property in addition to the town constables.

**Paragraph 2:**
<u>Point</u>: There was still an emphasis on collective responsibility and despite town constables and night watchmen locals were still expected to participate in hue and cry.
<u>Evidence (supporting own knowledge)</u>: Because the population of rural communities had not changed as much as in the towns and there was less need for appointed constables, the community was still expected to take a leading role in identifying and tracking down suspects using hue and cry if they witnessed a crime.

**Paragraph 3:**
<u>Point</u>: As well as expansion of the roles of town constable and night watchman a new role of thief taker developed to deal with rising crime rates.
<u>Evidence (supporting own knowledge)</u>: A thief taker was appointed and paid by a victim of crime to track down the suspect when other law enforcement methods had failed.

---

(1) Read the student's plan above and:

   (a) highlight 🖉 the two paragraphs that identify significant change (agreeing with the statement).

   (b) circle Ⓐ the paragraph that identifies a limitation in how significant change was during this period (disagreeing with the statement).

(2) Read the student's notes for paragraph 3, which are based on evidence from the student's own knowledge.

   (a) From your own knowledge, what other example could you use to argue that the **change** in the nature of **law enforcement** was or was not significant in the period **1500–1700**? Write 🖉 your answer below.

..................................................................................................................................

..................................................................................................................................

..................................................................................................................................

   (b) Give one reason why you chose that example. 🖉

..................................................................................................................................

..................................................................................................................................

..................................................................................................................................

..................................................................................................................................

# Crime and punishment, 1500–1900

This unit uses the theme of crime and punishment, 1500–1900, to build your skills in understanding change. If you need to review your knowledge of this theme, work through these pages.

(1) Write 🖉 explanations of why the following views led to the end of public execution.

| | | | |
|---|---|---|---|
| All humans are equal and therefore one human should not treat another inhumanely. | Executions being public meant the condemned had no dignity in their final minutes. | Public executions attracted large crowds and a 'carnival' atmosphere. | Large crowds provided opportunity for additional crimes such as pickpocketing and prostitution. |

(2) Transportation from Britain to Australia officially ended in 1868. Highlight 🖉 in one colour the statements that accurately describe Australian objections to transportation and in a different colour, highlight 🖉 the statements that describe the British arguments. Fill in 🖉 the colour code key to help you.

**Colour code:** Australian objections ⬚     British objections ⬚

| Ex-convicts were believed to be more likely to reoffend and were blamed for high crime rates in local towns. | Convict ships were inhumane according to some campaigners. | The gold rush had made Australia a desirable place to settle, so transportation was thought to be a less effective deterrent. | Convict workers meant lower wages or fewer available jobs for other locals. | People were concerned about running costs. | Up to the 19th century, prison had been used to house debtors and the accused in the run up to trial rather than as a punishment in its own right. As this purpose changed, more prisons were built in Britain. |

**(3)** Read statements A–I below, which tell the story of the changing role of the police. Number ✏ the statements 1–9 to show the correct chronological order.

**A** The Metropolitan Police Act gave every London district its own professional, uniformed police force. The main aim was a public presence on the streets of London. ☐

**B** Town constables worked alongside night watchmen and were expected to stop suspected criminals, break up fights and round up 'sturdy beggars'. ☐

**C** The Middlesex Justices Act set up further detective offices elsewhere in the country. ☐

**D** Henry Fielding, a magistrate, and his brother, set up the Bow Street Runners – a crime-fighting team in London. ☐

**E** CID at Scotland Yard – specialist detective branch of 16 'plain clothes' police officers who, instead of 'walking the beat', focused on investigation. ☐

**F** Locals were expected to join hue and cry to chase suspected criminals and bring them to justice. ☐

**G** The Bow Street Runners were officially paid by the government, making them the first modern detective force. ☐

**H** National Crimes Records and increasing use of new communication technology in policing led to improvement in information sharing across police forces. ☐

**I** The Police Act forced the setting up of local police forces. It was based on the idea of deterrence through detection – people would be less likely to commit a crime if they knew the police would be actively looking for them. ☐

**(4)** Read through the systems of punishment listed below. Which were predominant during c1500–c1700 and which continued to be used during the period c1750–c1900? Highlight ✏ the statements to show your decisions. Fill in ✏ the colour code to the key.

**Colour code:**    c1500–c1700 ☐          c1750–c1900 ☐

| | | |
|---|---|---|
| **Transportation** to the colonies – originally America and then following the war of independence to Australia. | **Public executions** to create spectacle and fear and act as a deterrent to crime. | **Mutilation** by branding the body or removing a digit or limb. |
| **Silent and separate systems** in prisons. Based on the belief that prison should involve hard work but that prisoners should be safe from one another. | **Fines** usually for breaking contracts or agreements or as compensation for damage caused to property or person. | **Pillory and stocks** punishment by public humiliation. Used for a wide variety of minor crimes such as dishonest shopkeeping or drunkeness. |

**(5)** Using your selections above:

**a** clarify one punishment which was no longer commonly used by the period 1700–1900 and explain why ✏

.................................................................................................................................

**b** clarify one punishment which continued to be used but explain one way in which it had changed or developed by 1900. ✏

.................................................................................................................................

# 1 How do I know what makes a change historically significant?

Make sure you respond appropriately to a question that asks you about the extent something changed. Remember: events themselves are not change. Rather, change is when the consequences of events are historically significant.

Sometimes when an **event** takes place it causes something to alter and therefore **change** also takes place.

This is why they are commonly confused.

However, there are times when an **event** takes place and nothing alters; therefore it is simply an **event**.

> An **event** is when something happens.
> A **change** is when something alters.

**1** **a** Read the statements below. Some are **descriptions of events** and some are **descriptions of change**. Highlight  the statements to show which are which. To help you, fill in  the colour code key.

**Colour code:**        Events ▢        Changes ▢

| | | |
|---|---|---|
| Oliver Cromwell became Lord Protector in 1653. | More people were burnt at the stake for heresy. | Vagabonds were harshly punished. |
| More poor people were forced to find work in new towns, and were treated as vagrants. | Henry VIII closed down the monasteries. | The Game Act of 1671 was introduced. |
| Vagrancy laws were brought in by the government. | A number of 'moral crimes' were introduced to control behaviour. | The Heresy Acts were reintroduced by Mary I. |

**b** Now complete the flow diagram below by writing  a summary of the descriptions above, so that each 'event' links to the 'change' it led to.

Event                                              Change

⟶

⟶

⟶

**How do I distinguish between change and continuity?**

It is a common misconception that continuity is simply the absence of change – small changes are happening all the time. Continuity is when the changes in a period lack historical significance. For example, after a General Election there may be a change in the political party running the country, but if they pursue similar policies to the previous party it may feel like a period of continuity. In the thematic study paper, the 16-mark exam question will often ask you about change and continuity between two dates, events or periods.

You can practise identifying change and continuity using timelines like the ones below.

**Timeline of changes in the nature of criminal activity**

| | Middle Ages | | | | Renaissance | | Industrial Revolution | 20th century to present |
|---|---|---|---|---|---|---|---|---|

| 1000 | 1100 | 1200 | 1300 | 1400 | 1500 | 1600 | 1700 | 1800 | 1900 | 2000 |

Crimes against authority

Witchcraft

Crimes against property

Crimes against the person

Moral crimes

Cyber crime

Race crime

**Timeline of changes in punishments**

| | Middle Ages | | | | Renaissance | | Industrial Revolution | 20th century to present |
|---|---|---|---|---|---|---|---|---|

| 1000 | 1100 | 1200 | 1300 | 1400 | 1500 | 1600 | 1700 | 1800 | 1900 | 2000 |

Death penalty

Mutilation

Fines

Transportation

Prison: hard labour

Prison: rehabilitation

1. Using the information in the timelines above, write 🖉 your answers to the following questions. During which time period was there:

   a) the most change in the nature of crimes? ............................................................................

   b) the most continuity in the nature of crimes? ......................................................................

   c) the most change in punishments? ...........................................................................................

   d) the most continuity in punishments? ......................................................................................

2. On a separate piece of paper, write 🖉 a bullet-point plan for a question that asks whether you agree:

   a) 1500–1700 was a period of change

   b) there was continuity between 1500 and 1900.

   > The timelines above may help you when writing your plans. The key questions to ask are: What was introduced? What stayed the same?

# 3 How do I decide how significant a change is?

When answering questions on change, you need to be able to identify and select those changes that are the most historically significant. You can determine the historical significance of changes by judging their impact using different criteria.

1 Read through the changes in the period c1500–c1700 listed below.

| | | | |
|---|---|---|---|
| **A** The population was growing and people were moving into the towns. This caused an increase in crime rates, especially in the towns. | **B** Some people had enough money to hire their own private guards to protect them and their property. | **C** Although the roles of town constable and night watchman had already been created, the force was expanded to cope with the rising crime rates. | **D** The role of thief taker was created as victims wanted to catch criminals the town constable had failed to bring to justice. |
| **E** Thief takers were well paid, which encouraged corruption. Some criminals operated as thief takers and informed on rivals to make money. | **F** Town constables became the first professional (paid) law enforcers. | **G** Between 1500 and 1700 the population of Britain increased by about 3 million. | **H** Successful and therefore wealthy merchants in towns became visible targets for crimes like robbery. |

For each criterion of significance below, select an example from the table above. (An example may fit in more than one criterion.) Write  the letter of your example in the table below and annotate  the most and least significant in the final column.

| Significance criteria | Example | Most/least significant |
|---|---|---|
| **Immediate impact:** This change had a big impact at the time it happened. People noticed their lives were different as a result. | | |
| **Impact on ideas:** People's ideas (e.g. feeling deterred from committing a crime) were significantly different as a result. | | |
| **Widespread impact:** This change affected a large number of people from different geographical areas of the world or from a range of different social groups. | | |
| **On-going impact:** This one change caused a number of other changes to happen (knock-on effects). | | |
| **Long-term impact:** The impact of this change continued to affect people's lives for a long time or still has an impact on how we live our lives today. | | |

Most significant has the most different kinds of impacts; least significant has the fewest or none.

# Sample response

Use what you have learned in this unit to complete the student's response to this exam-style question.

**Exam-style question**

'There was significant change in the nature of law enforcement in the period 1500–1700.' How far do you agree? Explain your answer.

You may use the following in your answer:

- town constables
- hue and cry.

You **must** also use information of your own.

(16 marks) + (4 marks)

(1) Use this checklist to assess each paragraph of the student's answer. ✓

| Checklist | Paragraph 1 | Paragraph 2 | Paragraph 3 |
|---|---|---|---|
| Has identified a **change** rather than simply an event | | | |
| Is focused on **change** rather than **continuity** | | | |
| Has identified **why** the change is significant/limited in significance | | | |

Paragraph 1:

Point: There was a significant change in law enforcement in the period 1500–1700, as the role of the town constable changed.

Evidence (supporting own knowledge): Town constables had already been introduced but the role was expanded to meet increased demand as crime rates went up. Crime rates were increasing due to the growth of populations in the town. People who had the money would appoint their own personal guard to protect their property in addition to the town constables.

Why was this a significant change?

Paragraph 2:

Point: However, there was still an emphasis on collective responsibility and despite town constables and night watchmen locals were still expected to participate in hue and cry.

Evidence (supporting own knowledge): Because the population of rural communities had not changed as much and there was less need for appointed constables, the community was still expected to take a leading role in identifying and tracking down suspects using hue and cry if they witnessed a crime.

Why was this a limitation to the significance of change?

Paragraph 3:

Point: As well as expansion of the roles of town constable and night watchman, the new role of thief taker developed to deal with rising crime rates.

Evidence (supporting own knowledge): A thief taker was appointed and paid by a victim of crime to track down the suspect when other law enforcement methods had failed.

Why was this a significant change?

Conclusion:

Although there were some similar roles being used to enforce the law between 1500 and 1700, there was a lot more dependence on the professional forces and less reliance on collective responsibility, as a result of the rising population and changing communities.

# Your turn!

Now try planning and writing your own answer to the following exam-style question.

### Exam-style question

'The nature of crimes changed significantly during the period 1700–1900.' How far do you agree? Explain your answer.

You may use the following in your answer:

- smuggling

- poaching.

You **must** also use information of your own.                    (16 marks) + (4 marks)

> Plan to write three paragraphs, developing three separate lines of argument that answer the question. (Note that paragraph 3 can be used to either agree or disagree with the statement.)

① Write ✏ a plan for your answer below before writing it out in full on a separate sheet of paper.

| Paragraph 1: The nature of crime changed little... | Paragraph 2: The nature of crime changed significantly... |
|---|---|
| Point (identify a **continuity**): | Point (identify a **change**): |
| Evidence (detail of what **stayed the same**; before and after): | Evidence (detail of what **changed**; before and after): |
| Explanation (why this **continuity** was significant): | Explanation (why this **change** was significant): |

| Paragraph 3: Separate line of argument that either agrees or disagrees with the statement | Conclusion: |
|---|---|
| Point (identify another **change** or **continuity**): | |
| Evidence (detail of what **changed** or **stayed the same**; before and after): | |
| Explanation (why this **change** or **continuity** was significant): | |

> You could use the second timeline on page 56 to first select relevant examples of change and then give each a significance rating.

# Review your skills

## Check up

Review your response to the exam-style question on page 59. Tick ✓ the column to show how well you think you have done each of the following.

| | Had a go ✓ | Nearly there ✓ | Got it! ✓ |
|---|---|---|---|
| identified a significant change, relevant to the question, and explained why it was significant | ☐ | ☐ | ☐ |
| identified a continuity or limitation to the significance of the changes, relevant to the question, and explained why it was significant | ☐ | ☐ | ☐ |
| made a judgement about whether the period was one of continuity | ☐ | ☐ | ☐ |

## Need more practice?

If you want to practise another exam-style question, try ✐ this one on a separate piece of paper.

### Exam-style question

'The campaigns of individuals were the main reason for changes in the prison service in the period 1800–2000.' How far do you agree? Explain your answer.

You may use the following in your answer:

- Elizabeth Fry

- rehabilitation.

You **must** also use information of your own.                    (16 marks) + (4 marks)

How confident do you feel about each of these **skills**? Colour ✐ in the bars.

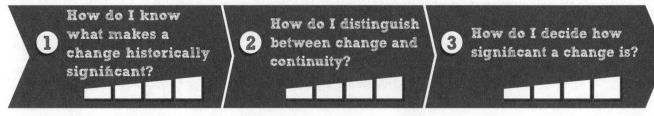

1 How do I know what makes a change historically significant?

2 How do I distinguish between change and continuity?

3 How do I decide how significant a change is?

# (7) Making links between points

This unit will help you to develop the vocabulary and understanding necessary to make links between points in your answers. The skills you will build are to:

- acquire appropriate language to make links
- develop into explanations by making links between points
- show links between key aspects of the question to support your analysis.

In the exam, you will be asked to tackle questions such as the one below. This unit will prepare you to write your own response to this exam-style question.

---

**Exam-style question**

'The death of Matthew Hopkins was the main reason witchcraft became less common by 1700.'

How far do you agree? Explain your answer.

You may use the following in your answer:

- the Royal Society

- greater social stability.

You **must** also use information of your own.                    (16 marks) + (4 marks)

---

The three key questions in the **skills boosts** will help you to identify and use linking phrases and to support your analysis by making links between supporting detail and the question.

**1** How do I know when to use linking phrases?

**2** How do I make links to develop my supporting knowledge?

**3** How do I link my ideas and supporting detail back to the question?

Look at this student's first paragraph in response to the exam-style question on page 61.

> The hysteria about witchcraft certainly went into decline after the death of Matthew Hopkins. Hopkins had been a lawyer who called himself the Witchfinder General when he set about hunting down witches in the east of England. In order to find potential witches Hopkins would encourage accusations based on suspicions. There was a significant financial reward to people who successfully uncovered witchery and this motivated Hopkins to stir up hysteria and create as many 'leads' as possible. People could receive the equivalent of a month's wages for each accused witch. When Hopkins died, therefore, so too did a lot of the rumour and hearsay of the witch hunts and there was a noticeable fall in prosecutions.

**1** **a** Read the student's response. Rewrite the narrative (supporting details) as a flow chart.

**b** Select an explanation link from the table and write its letter on each arrow, to show how the details have been linked together.

| Explanation links |
|---|
| A ... when he set about... |
| B In order to... |
| C ... therefore it was in Hopkins's interest to... |
| D ... so too did... |

**2** The list below gives some examples of cause and consequence linking phrases. Highlight the cause-linking phrases in one colour, and the consequence-linking phrases in another. Fill in the colour code key to help you. Some may be used for both purposes.

**Colour code:** Cause ☐          Consequence ☐

| | | |
|---|---|---|
| this meant that | therefore | so too did |
| as a result | creating the potential to | in the hope of |
| in order to | this contributed to | this influenced |
| increased the chances of | noticed the link between | it was not until |

# Witchcraft and the law, 1500–1700

This unit uses the theme of witchcraft and the law, 1500–1700, to build your skills in making links between points. If you need to review your knowledge of this theme, work through these pages.

**1** **a** Write the three main reasons why witchcraft came to be viewed and punished more severely by the authorities during the period 1500–1700.

1 ..................................................................................................................................................

2 ..................................................................................................................................................

3 ..................................................................................................................................................

**b** What was the main factor in the decline of witchcraft accusations by 1700?

...............................................................................................................................................................

...............................................................................................................................................................

**2** Look at the developments in the decline of witch hunts below. Write the letters A–F in the relevant positions on the pyramid, to show which you think was the most and least influential development.

**A** Matthew Hopkins (Witchfinder General) died in 1647. He had helped to stir up hysteria about witches and after his death people became less concerned.

**B** People were increasingly prepared to question the evidence. They were not denying the existence of witchcraft but demanding clearer evidence for conviction.

**C** The Enlightenment was a philosophical movement, popular in Europe during the 17th and 18th centuries, which demanded a more scientific approach to all aspects of life.

**D** The founding of the Royal Society in 1660 brought together scientific thinkers to share and discuss ideas.

**E** Changing public attitudes towards more rational thought about witchcraft meant it began to be recognised as a superstitious idea rather than a crime.

**F** Greater religious stability and less social upheaval by 1700 meant the climate of fear had gone.

Most influential

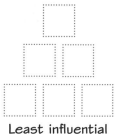

Least influential

**3** Look at the summary details of the story of witchcraft below. Write 🖉 the letter of each stage in the correct column in the table below, to show whether it caused the rise or decline in witchcraft accusations in Britain.

> **A** There was a general belief in witchcraft fuelled by religious fears.

> **B** James I was an enthusiastic witch hunter and wrote a book on the subject in 1597 called *Demonologie*.

> **C** In 1647 Witchfinder General Matthew Hopkins died of tuberculosis.

> **D** In the 17th century the role of women was very restricted and they were expected to focus on domestic duties. Women who did not meet society's expectations (i.e. by not marrying, etc.) were treated with suspicion.

> **E** In 1660 the Royal Society was established in London, advocating scientific reasoning.

> **F** The Enlightenment was a philosophical movement of the 17th and 18th centuries which focused on the use of reason rather than superstition.

| Rise | Decline |
|---|---|
|  |  |

**4** Draw 🖉 lines linking each of the features on the left to the most accurate explanation of how they led to a rise in accusations of witchcraft on the right.

| | |
|---|---|
| **A** Matthew Hopkins | **a** Witchcraft was part of the old struggle between good and evil. It was believed that getting rid of witches would 'cleanse' society. |
| **B** The role of the Church | **b** Massive social disruption and uncertainty can lead to people being more attracted to superstitious ideas – believing in magic rather than reason and logic. |
| **C** The English Civil War | **c** The significant financial reward was based on the number of trials being heard. The more accusations, the more trials, the more money. |

**How do I know when to use linking phrases?**

Use linking phrases to avoid writing a list of 'what happened' and to ensure the knowledge you are describing supports your answer to the question. Linking phrases can also explain why someone does something (for example, 'in hope of…') or link a consequence back to the action ('as a result of…').

**(1)** Circle (A) the phrases used in the sample answer on page 62.

| | | |
|---|---|---|
| this meant that | therefore | so too did |
| as a result | creating the potential to | in the hope of |
| in order to | this contributed to | this influenced |
| increased the chances of | noticed the link between | it was not until |

**(2)** **a** Tick (✓) which of the following student responses uses linking phrases and so avoids writing a list of what happened.

**b** Now highlight (✏) the linking phrases.

☐ Hopkins was a lawyer. He called himself the Witchfinder General. He hunted down witches for money.

☐ Hopkins was a lawyer in Essex and East Anglia who called himself the Witchfinder General. He stirred up hysteria about witchcraft in the hope of finding as many witches as possible by encouraging people to make accusations based on suspicions. The financial rewards for each witch accused gave Hopkins the incentive to build superstitious attitudes as much as possible.

☐ Hopkins was a lawyer in Essex and East Anglia. He encouraged people to accuse women of witchcraft. The more people he accused the more money he made.

**(3)** Read the following passage. Rewrite (✏) it below, but this time add some linking phrases, to link the description together. You can select phrases from the box in **(1)** to help.

> The hysteria and superstitious attitudes surrounding witchcraft certainly went into decline after the death of Matthew Hopkins. Hopkins had been a lawyer who called himself the Witchfinder General when he set about hunting down witches in the east of England. Hopkins would encourage accusations based on suspicions. There was a significant financial reward to people who successfully uncovered witchery. It was in Hopkins's interest to stir up hysteria.

.....................................................................................................................................
.....................................................................................................................................
.....................................................................................................................................
.....................................................................................................................................
.....................................................................................................................................
.....................................................................................................................................
.....................................................................................................................................
.....................................................................................................................................

# ② How do I make links to develop my supporting knowledge?

By linking rather than listing supporting details, you will start to develop your explanations. Think carefully about the meaning of each linking phrase and select the most appropriate to develop the point you are making.

① The following phrases can be used to build on detail used in your answer.

  **a** Circle Ⓐ phrases to link causes and consequences.

  **b** Underline Ⓐ phrases to link ideas about similarities.

| | | | |
|---|---|---|---|
| In addition… | Furthermore… | Consequently… | Such as… |
| In contrast… | Evidence of… | For example… | Although… |
| In support of… | Similarly… | Equally important… | Made possible… |
| As a result of… | In spite of… | Compared to… | As well as… |
| Therefore… | Since… | Despite… | On the other hand… |

② The two details below would make good supporting knowledge in a paragraph on why Matthew Hopkins had caused an increase in hysteria about witchcraft (in response to the exam-style question on page 61).

  **a** Link ✏ the details by selecting a suitable linking phrase.

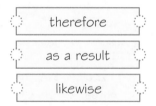

> There were significant financial rewards for each person who accused a witch

- therefore
- as a result
- likewise

> … Hopkins had an incentive to stir up as much superstition and hysteria about witchcraft as he possibly could.

  **b** Try out the other linking phrases to complete the sentence. Does the linking phrase you have selected make a difference to the meaning or effectiveness of the sentence? If so, why? ✏

  .........................................................................................................................................................................

  .........................................................................................................................................................................

③ In this answer extract, the student wants to show that, in order to find witches, Hopkins needed to create hysteria surrounding witchcraft.

> *In order to find potential witches, Hopkins would encourage accusations based on suspicions.*

  **a** Circle Ⓐ the linking phrase the student has used.

  **b** **i** Annotate ✏ the answer with some alternative linking phrases and then read the sentence with every option, to check which is best.

   **ii** Write ✏ your final choice of linking phrase below.

  .........................................................................................................................................................................

## 3 How do I link my ideas and supporting detail back to the question?

Different linking phrases will have different purposes in your writing, so it is important to be clear about what the question is asking you to do.

1. Complete ✐ the table by sorting the following linking phrases from the word box into the correct column to describe the purpose of the linking phrase.

| such as | this motivated | however |
| as a result | whereas | in the hope of |
| this hindered | this contributed to | this influenced |
| increased the chances of | noticed the link between | in contrast |

| To compare and contrast ideas | To give examples of an idea | To show cause |
| --- | --- | --- |
| | For example... | |

2. Your opening sentence of each paragraph should also be a linking phrase that makes it clear you intend to answer the question.

Tick ✓ the opening sentence below that most effectively addresses the question on page 61.

A ☐

*Matthew Hopkins had made a living from hunting witches.*

B ☐

*One of the most significant reasons for the decline in superstitious attitudes and witchcraft was the death of self-styled Witchfinder General, Matthew Hopkins, who had whipped up hysteria for his own financial gain.*

'How far do you agree' questions require you to write more than one paragraph, as you need to evaluate two opposing arguments and write a balanced response. By linking these two paragraphs you will produce a more effective answer.

3. a In the opening sentence you ticked in question 2, underline Ⓐ a phrase that shows the paragraph is agreeing with the statement.

b Decide whether you will add an example, a comparison or an explanation of cause/consequence. Circle Ⓐ your choice below.

| an example | a comparison | an explanation of cause/consequence |

c Highlight ✐ the linking phrases in the table in 1 that you might use to continue this paragraph and explain why superstitious attitudes and witchcraft were becoming less common by 1700. Write ✐ your continuation below.

..............................................................................................................................

..............................................................................................................................

d Highlight ✐ the linking phrases in the table in 1 that would be appropriate ways to start a second paragraph arguing that superstitious attitudes and witchcraft were **not** becoming less common by 1700. Remember to choose an opening sentence that clearly addresses the question.

**Unit 7 Making links between points    67**

# Sample response

Use what you have learned in this unit to improve on the student's use of linking vocabulary in their response to this exam-style question.

**Exam-style question**

'The death of Matthew Hopkins was the main reason witchcraft became less common by 1700.' How far do you agree? Explain your answer.

You may use the following in your answer:

- the Royal Society

- greater social stability.

You **must** also use information of your own.                    **(16 marks) + (4 marks)**

---

The hysteria about witchcraft certainly went into decline after the death of Matthew Hopkins. Hopkins had been a lawyer who called himself the Witchfinder General when he set about hunting down witches in the east of England. In order to find potential witches Hopkins would encourage accusations based on suspicions. There was a significant financial reward to people who successfully uncovered witchery and this motivated Hopkins to stir up hysteria and create as many 'leads' as possible. People could receive the equivalent of a month's wages for each accused witch. When Hopkins died, therefore, so too did a lot of the rumour and hearsay of the witch hunts and there was a noticeable fall in prosecutions.

---

**(1)** Look at the student's first paragraph.

**a** Underline (A) any phrases that link parts of the narrative (supporting details) to each other.

**b** Circle (A) any phrases that link the narrative to the question being asked.

**c** Note down (✎) as many alternative linking phrases as you can think of for the one you underlined in part **a**.

........................................................................................................

........................................................................................................

........................................................................................................

........................................................................................................

**d** Write (✎) which alternative linking phrase you would use from your examples above.

........................................................................................................

**(2)** The student wants to make the counter argument that Matthew Hopkins's death was not the main reason for the decline in witchcraft by 1700 in their next paragraph. How would you start this paragraph? Write (✎) a full sentence to start the paragraph.

........................................................................................................

........................................................................................................

........................................................................................................

**Remember:**

- you must show that you intend to compare and possibly contrast this point with previous points made. Aim to use language in your opening sentence to show this. Task 2 asks you for a contrasting point, so use phrases like 'However...' or 'On the other hand...'

- you must also refer back to the question. Do this by using words from it in your answer, then you will be clear about how this point is going to answer the question.

# Your turn!

Now try this exam-style question using the skills you have built in this unit.

'The most important factor in explaining witch hunts in the years c1500–1700 was religion.' How far do you agree? Explain your answer.

You may use the following in your answer:

- *Demonologie* (1597)

- the English Civil War.

You **must** also use information of your own.                    (16 marks) + (4 marks)

**(1)** Use the following template to plan ✏ your answer.

| Argument | Counter argument |
|---|---|
| | |
| Opening phrase | Opening phrase |
| | |

| Knowledge details to support this point: | Possible linking phrases: | Knowledge details to support this point: | Possible linking phrases: |
|---|---|---|---|
| | | | |

**(2)** Now decide on your conclusion by completing ✏ the following. Remember to link back to the reasons you were most convinced by to explain your judgement.

I agree with the statement ☐

I disagree with the statement ☐

Because:

I was convinced by the argument that religion played a significant role ☐

I was convinced by the argument that another factor played a significant role ☐

I was not convinced by the argument that religion played a very significant role ☐

other (explain what and why) ...................................................................................................

.................................................................................................................................................

You can find more guidance on writing conclusions in Unit 8.

# Review your skills

## Check up

Review your response to the exam-style question on page 69. Tick ✓ the column to show how well you think you have done each of the following.

| | Had a go ✓ | Nearly there ✓ | Got it! ✓ |
|---|---|---|---|
| considered the purpose of linking phrases and selected the most appropriate to support the point made | ☐ | ☐ | ☐ |
| selected a range of linking phrases to develop knowledge used rather than listing relevant details | ☐ | ☐ | ☐ |
| thought carefully about opening phrases that link effectively back to the question | ☐ | ☐ | ☐ |

## Need more practice?

You will need to practise what has been covered in this unit to answer all the other exam-style questions in this workbook. If you want to practise another exam-style question, try ✏ this one on a separate piece of paper.

### Exam-style question

'The most important factor in explaining the decline in witchcraft accusations in the years c1600–1700 was the growth of scientific thinking.'

How far do you agree? Explain your answer.

You may use the following in your answer:

• the Witchcraft Act (1735)

• the Royal Society.

You **must** also use information of your own.                    (16 marks) + (4 marks)

How confident do you feel about each of these **skills**? Colour ✏ in the bars.

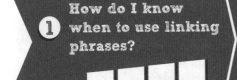

**1** How do I know when to use linking phrases?

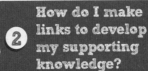

**2** How do I make links to develop my supporting knowledge?

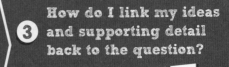

**3** How do I link my ideas and supporting detail back to the question?

# ⑧ Making a judgement

This unit will help you to make judgements and reach conclusions through prioritising of arguments and expressing evaluations.

The skills you will build are to:

- prioritise information to develop your analysis
- recognise and challenge generalisations
- move from the specific to the general without being overwhelmed by too many facts.

In the exam, you will be asked to tackle a question such as the one below. This unit will prepare you to write your own response to the question below.

**Exam-style question**

'The role of prisons changed significantly during the period 1700–1900.' How far do you agree? Explain your answer.

You may use the following in your answer:

- separate and silent
- humanitarianism.

You **must** also use information of your own.

(16 marks) + (4 marks)

The three key questions in the **skills boosts** will help you prioritise details to reach an appropriate judgement.

 **1 How do I make judgements?**

 **2 How do I organise information to reach a judgement?**

**3 How do I make a 'good' judgement?**

Look at this student's plan and completed conclusion in response to the exam-style question on page 71.

---

**Paragraph A: Change – purpose and conditions**
- At start of 19th century it was believed that prison sentences should be a deterrent:
  - they should involve hard labour and pay back to society
  - prisoners were forced to live and work in silence and were kept separate from other inmates – silent and separate system
- Humanitarianism – no person (including criminals) should be treated inhumanely
- Reformers such as Elizabeth Fry and John Howard
- The main purpose of prison should be rehabilitation – this set the tone for changes to the role of prisons by 2000
- Education and training to prepare people for returning to society
- Open prisons to support reintegration

**Paragraph B: continuity in the role of prisons**
- Still limits what a criminal is able to do – limits freedoms
- Still aspects that are aimed to be a deterrent to crime
- Continued use of prisons for remand – to hold suspects awaiting trial

**Conclusion:**
Individuals such as Elizabeth Fry and John Howard and the humanitarian ideas they followed were highly influential in changing society's view of prison. Although we continue to use prisons to limit convicts' freedoms and as a deterrent to crime, conditions are much improved and rehabilitation, including alternatives to custodial sentences, is prioritised.

---

(1) Cross out (~~out~~) the option below to reflect what the student has written in their conclusion.

> The student thinks that prisons **did/did not** change significantly in the period 1700–1900.

(2) How does the student justify their answer? Highlight (✐) the details in the student's conclusion that they use to support their judgement.

(3) The student plans to explain that prisons did not change significantly in the period 1700–1900 in the second paragraph. The silent and separate system and humanitarianism are given in the question, which also asks for a third point of argument – 'information of your own'.

   (a) What development would you pick to compare to the silent and separate system and humanitarianism and why? (✐)

   ...................................................................................................................................................

   ...................................................................................................................................................

   ...................................................................................................................................................

   (b) Would your chosen development change the judgement in the student's conclusion? Why? (✐)

   ...................................................................................................................................................

   ...................................................................................................................................................

   ...................................................................................................................................................

# Changing attitudes to punishment, 1500–2000

This unit uses the theme of changing attitudes to punishment, 1500–2000, to build your skills in making a judgement. If you need to review your knowledge of this theme, work through these pages.

**1** Draw ✏ lines to link the examples on the right to the correct 'factor of influence' in changing punishments by 2000, on the left.

| A Role of the individual |

| **a** Electronic tagging to control a convict outside of a prison environment by setting and monitoring limits on where they go and when. |

| B Changing ideas and attitudes |

| **b** The Young Persons Act 1933. Raised the age of the death sentence to 18. |

| C Developments in science and technology |

| **c** Elizabeth Fry's campaign for reform of the prison service during the early 19th century. She wanted improvement in living standards in prison and more focus on education and rehabilitation. |

| D Role of the government |

| **d** Alternatives to prison sentences that encourage rehabilitation. For example, restorative justice or drug and alcohol treatment programmes. |

**2** In your own words describe ✏ the difference between punishment as a deterrent and a method of rehabilitation.

....................................................................................................................................

....................................................................................................................................

**3** Describe ✏ one difference between the way adults and younger offenders are punished today.

....................................................................................................................................

....................................................................................................................................

**4** Which ✏ factor do you think was most influential in ending capital punishment and why?

....................................................................................................................................

....................................................................................................................................

(5) The table below contains a number of statements regarding deterrents and the rehabilitation of offenders from 1900 to the present day.

Highlight 🖉 deterrents that 'pay back to society' in one colour and rehabilitation methods in another. Fill in 🖉 the colour code key to help you.

**Colour code:** Deterrent that pays back to society ⬜          Rehabilitation ⬜

| | | |
|---|---|---|
| In 1907 probation officers were employed to check on offenders living outside of prison. | In 1933 New Hall in Wakefield was opened. This was the first open prison. Prisoners could take part in work programmes and gradually reintegrate into society. | In 1908 The Prevention of Crime Act created a national system of borstals for young offenders. They were very disciplined and structured but made time for work programmes and learning practical skills. |
| Electronic tagging introduced in 1990s to control, monitor and limit the behaviour of offenders living outside of prison. | In 1969 a law was put in place which encouraged the courts to favour care orders and supervision by social workers for young offenders. | Restorative justice arranges a supervised meeting between offender and victim (or victim's family) to help offenders understand the consequences of their actions. |
| Capital punishment existed until 1965, when it was abolished for all crimes except high treason and violent piracy (abolished in 1998). | Community service introduced in 1970s to improve local communities. | Anti-Social Behaviour Orders (ASBOs) place restrictions on where a person can go or with whom they can have contact. |
| Mass video surveillance allows the police and private companies to monitor online activity and CCTV to forecast acts of terrorism and crime. | In 1980s the government encouraged Neighbourhood Watch schemes to protect local communities through organised communication with the police. | Breathalysers and speed cameras catch offenders and provide evidence of road crimes, leading to fines or possibly prosecution in court. |

(6) (a) Select one form of rehabilitation from the table above and explain 🖉 its benefits.

..................................................................................................................................................

..................................................................................................................................................

..................................................................................................................................................

(b) Circle 🅐 the factor below that motivated the majority of these changes.

| attitudes          technology          government |
|---|

# 1 How do I make judgements?

When making a judgement, you need to consider the criteria by which you judge **significance**. You may have evidence of how attitudes toward the purpose of prisons changed, but how do you decide if this was as significant as the continued use of prisons as a deterrent to crime?

**1** In the extract below, the student argues that the continued use of prisons as a deterrent to crime was the most significant. Annotate their argument showing where they have used the measures of significance which are listed in the table below.

> Prisons changed little in the period 1800–2000 as they were still intended to be a deterrent against crime. Life in prison continued to be made less desirable than living outside of prison. Despite humanitarian campaigns, change was relatively slow during the early 19th century. This is illustrated in the 1865 Prisons Act, which aimed to enforce a strict, uniform regime of punishment in all prisons. Prisoners were expected to do physical labour and meals were boring and repetitive. Freedoms were still severely restricted, and until the late 20th century there were no alternatives to incarceration.

| Measures of significance | Feature 1 ✓ | Score | Feature 2 ✓ | Score |
|---|---|---|---|---|
| **Change** – How much changed/stayed the same? | | | | |
| **Perception** – Did people at the time notice the impact? | | | | |
| **Longevity** – Did this factor continue to have an impact for a long time? | | | | |
| **Inspiration** – Did this factor cause other significant developments? | | | | |
| **Scale** – Who was affected by this factor (locally, nationally, globally)? | | | | |
| Totals | | | | |

**2** **a** Write ✏ two features of changing attitudes towards the purpose of prisons in the period 1700–1900.

Feature 1: ......................................................................................................................................................

Now add a description of this feature using your own subject knowledge: ........................................

..............................................................................................................................................................................

..............................................................................................................................................................................

Feature 2: ......................................................................................................................................................

Now add a description of this feature using your own subject knowledge: ........................................

..............................................................................................................................................................................

..............................................................................................................................................................................

**b** Tick ✓ the chart above to indicate which measures of significance each feature has.

**c** Which ✏ feature had more ticks for points of significance?

**3** **a** Repeat the task, but give each point of significance a score out of 5 for each feature, where 5 = very significant (biggest impact) and 0 = no significance (no tick). ✏

**b** Then total up each score column. Record ✏ your findings.

# ② How do I organise information to reach a judgement?

In your conclusions you will need to make a judgement. Before you can do this you need to have explored the argument for and the argument against. This skills boost aims to help you select which arguments to explore in order to reach a judgement.

Look again at the exam-style question below, taken from page 71. The highlighted section indicates the focus of the question, from which you will select your points of argument. Having selected relevant details you will need to organise information to support your ideas. To do this effectively you need to identify the two most significant arguments to compare. These are the arguments you will want to explore.

**Exam-style question**

'The role of prisons changed significantly during the period 1700–1900.' How far do you agree? Explain your answer.

You may use the following in your answer:

• separate and silent

• humanitarianism.

You **must** also use information of your own.                    (16 marks) + (4 marks)

① Below is a list of some developments you may consider when answering this question. Remember, the silent and separate system and humanitarianism are given to you in the question, so if you use both of these you will need to make a third point using details from your own knowledge.

| **A** Silent and separate system | **B** Humanitarianism | **C** The work of key individuals |

| **D** Prisons and remand centres to hold suspects before trial | **E** Improvement in conditions | **F** Prisons as a deterrent to crime |

**a** Consider the significance of the impact of each of the above developments A–F on the role of prisons, then add ✎ each letter to the chart below in the first column under whether you think they are most, less or least significant.

**b** Write ✎ an explanation for your decisions in the spaces provided.

| Most significant □ | This development had the biggest impact (significance) because ................................................................................................................................................................................................................................ |
|---|---|
| Less significant □ □ | These two developments are less significant because ................................................ ................................................................................................ But they are more significant than the three developments below. |
| Least significant □ □ □ | These are the least significant because ................................................ ................................................................................................................................................................................................................ |

The developments in rows 1 and 2 are the ones you will use in your answer, as they are the most significant. They are the arguments you will want to evaluate.

#  How do I make a 'good' judgement?

You will know you have made a 'good' judgement if you are able to support your judgement with evidence that your selected argument is the most convincing – why is Argument X more significant than Argument Y if both are valid arguments? Don't forget, however, that there is no 'right' judgement!

(1) An effective conclusion should meet the following criteria:

**a** **It must reach a clear judgement.**

Which of the two features of changing attitudes towards the purpose of prisons that you selected on page 75 (1) a did you rank as most significant? Write it into the sentence below.

> Make sure judgements and supporting details have already been mentioned – avoid introducing new ideas at this stage.

*I believe attitudes towards the purpose of prisons changed significantly in the period c1700–1900 due to*

......................................................................................................................................

......................................................................................................................................

**b** **It must state what made one feature more significant.**

Write what made your feature above so significant into the sentence below.

> Consider the criteria of significance that scored highly: it continued to have an impact on the role of prisons for generations **or** it caused further changes in the role of prisons **or** it affected a large number of people etc.

.............................................. *was significant to changing attitudes because* ...............................

......................................................................................................................................

**c** **It must state what made one feature less significant.**

Write what made the other feature less significant into the sentence below.

> This feature may have scored highly in one area of the criteria but be less significant overall **or** it may have scored in every section, making it generally significant, but lacking in significance in any one area.

.............................................. *was not as significant because* ...............................................

......................................................................................................................................

(2) To write a good answer to this type of exam question you must consider ideas beyond the two given in the question. Plan a third paragraph on a separate piece of paper detailing another significant change or continuity in the role of prisons during the period 1700–1900 (see the suggestions in (1) on page 76 to help you).

# Sample response

Look again at the student's plan on page 72 for answering the exam-style question on page 71. Now look at their plan for a third paragraph below.

> **Paragraph C: Improved conditions**
> - living conditions had been unsanitary and these were improved based on humanitarian ideas
> - hard labour like forcing prisoners to walk treadmills for up to eight hours a day ended in favour of training

**(1)** You are now going to determine which of the following three conclusions gives the most effective judgement.

**a** Read the criteria (A–C) below and read the conclusions (1–3). Tick ✓ the box if the judgement has met that criterion.

**Criteria:**

**A:** Answer makes a clear judgement

**B:** Answer explains why chosen feature is significant

**C:** Answer explains why other feature(s) is/are less significant

| Judgement | Criteria | ✓ |
|---|---|---|
| 1. By 2000 prisons were still being used as remand centres to hold suspects awaiting trial. This is a role they had played in 1800 as well, so there was little significant change in the role of prisons during this period. | A / B / C | |
| 2. There was significant change in the role of prisons during the period 1800–2000, especially in terms of people's attitudes. This was partly due to the spread of humanitarian ideas. Humanitarians believed that no person, including criminals, should be treated inhumanely and this is a belief that continues to govern our society to this day – as does the role of rehabilitation in prison. As a result, hard labour ended and sanitary conditions in prisons were improved by 1900. However, conditions were not improved so far that prison was no longer a deterrent. The main purpose of prisons continued to be, and still is, to deter people from committing crime. To ensure this, prisons continued to apply strict limitations on a person's freedoms. For this reason, although the conditions of prisons changed, the role of prisons did not change significantly in the period 1800–2000. | A / B / C | |
| 3. I believe that, despite changing attitudes and the work of individuals, prison changed little in the period 1800–2000 as they were still intended to be a deterrent against crime. Life in prison continued to be made less desirable than living outside of prison. Despite humanitarian campaigns aimed at bringing an end to the silent and separate system, freedoms were and still are severely restricted and by 2000 there were no alternatives to incarceration. Although conditions slowly improved, the intentions of prisons changed very little. | A / B / C | |

**b** Circle Ⓐ which answer you think gives the best judgement.

| Judgement 1 | Judgement 2 | Judgement 3 |
|---|---|---|

# Your turn!

Use some of the planning techniques you have learned to write an answer to the exam-style question below.

**Exam-style question**

'In the period 1500–1800 the main reason for changes to punishments was retribution.'
How far do you agree? Explain your answer.
You may use the following in your answer:

- bloody code
- humanitarianism.

You **must** also use information of your own.           (16 marks) + (4 marks)

**(1)** In the table below, write two changes to the nature of crimes and two changes in punishments. Below each, start to plan the arguments for it and note some judgements about the significance. ✏️

The measures of significance may help you: Change, Perception, Longevity, Inspiration and Scale. See page 75 for detail on them.

| Change to punishments inspired by retribution | Change to punishments inspired by rehabilitation |
|---|---|
| Arguments: | Arguments: |
| Judgements about significance: | Judgements about significance: |

| A third change (not listed in question) inspired by either retribution or rehabilitation |
|---|
| Arguments: |
| Judgements about significance: |

**(2)** **a** Complete ✏️ the table below to rank the significance of your arguments in **(1)**. Make sure you include changes in punishments **and** the nature of crime.

| Most significant | This development had the biggest impact (significance) on changing punishments because ............................................................. ......................................................................................... |
|---|---|
| Less significant | These developments are less significant because ........................... ...................................................................... But they are more significant than the developments below. |
| Least significant | These are the least significant because ........................................ ......................................................................................... |

**b** Overall, which do you think was more significant in bringing about changes in punishments in the period 1500–1800 – retribution or rehabilitation? Circle Ⓐ your judgement.

**(3)** Now write ✏️ either the whole answer or a conclusion with a justified judgement on a separate sheet of paper.

# Review your skills

## Check up

Review your response to the exam-style question on page 79. Tick ✓ the column to show how well you think you have done each of the following.

| | Had a go ✓ | Nearly there ✓ | Got it! ✓ |
|---|---|---|---|
| selected relevant and significant points of argument, ensuring they covered both sides of the question | ☐ | ☐ | ☐ |
| explained the significance of each point of the argument | ☐ | ☐ | ☐ |
| reached a judgement in the conclusion, which identified the point of argument believed to be most significant | ☐ | ☐ | ☐ |
| justified the judgement made using the criteria for judging significance and based on ideas and details explained in the paragraphs | ☐ | ☐ | ☐ |

## Need more practice?

You will need to practise what has been covered in this unit to answer other exam-style questions in this workbook. If you want to practise another question, try ✐ this one:

### Exam-style question

'Attitudes in society were the most important factor influencing changes to punishments in the period c1500–2000.' How far do you agree? Explain your answer.

You may use the following in your answer:

- capital punishment
- conscientious objectors.

You **must** also use information of your own.                    (16 marks) + (4 marks)

How confident do you feel about each of these **skills**? Colour ✐ in the bars.

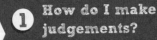

**1** How do I make judgements?

**2** How do I organise information to reach a judgement?

**3** How do I make a 'good' judgement?

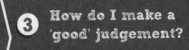

# Answers

## Unit 1

### Page 2

**(1)** and **(2)** During the 1840s many young Irishmen arrived in London on their way to America. When their money ran out, they stayed and worked as navvies. ~~These were labourers on the canals, roads and railways.~~ Many settled in Whitechapel increasing the overcrowding in this working-class district of London. In 1881 the Tsar of Russia was assassinated and people blamed Jewish people causing them to flee to London. The difference in cultures meant they often kept themselves separate from the rest of the Whitechapel community.

**(3)** **Feature 1:** Many settled in Whitechapel increasing the overcrowding in this working-class district of London.

**Feature 2:** The difference in cultures meant they often kept themselves separate from the rest of the Whitechapel community.

### Page 3

**(1)** b and d

**(2)** Circle: Theft of personal property; Stealing/robbery; begging; disruptive behaviour

**(3)** A – d; B – a; C – b; D – c

### Page 4

**(4)** A – d; B – b; C – a; D – c

**(5)** **a** Irish **c** Jewish

**b** Anarchists **d** Socialists

### Page 5

**(1)** A: Describe **two** features of Jewish immigration to Whitechapel.

B: Describe **two** features of anarchism in Whitechapel.

**(2)** a and b

| Question A | Question B |
|---|---|
| Were resented by the local workers of Whitechapel | Were often considered to be terrorists. |
| Came mainly from Eastern Europe, fleeing persecution. | Often came to Britain fleeing arrest. |
| Student's own response. | Student's own response. |

### Page 6

**(1)** A – c; B – a; C – d; D - b

**(2)** Student's own response.

### Page 7

**(1)** Student's own response.

### Page 8

**(1)** socialism in Whitechapel

**(2)** and **(4)**

Socialists wanted to bring down the capitalist system in Britain to create a fairer spread of wealth. They believed it was unfair that only a few people benefited from the money made by industry. Capitalism was when businesses were privately owned and investors can decide how money made from that industry was used. ~~The first socialist party had been founded in Britain in 1881 and there was hope that they may be able to get a local councillor elected in Whitechapel due to the large number of working class residents there, whom they represented.~~

**(3)** 2/4

**(5)** **Feature:** Student's own response.

**Supporting detail:** Student's own response.

### Page 9

**(1)** Describe two features of the Irish immigrant community in Whitechapel.

**(2)**, **(3)**, and **(4)** Student's own response.

## Unit 2

### Page 12

**(1)** Student's own response.

### Page 13

**(1)**

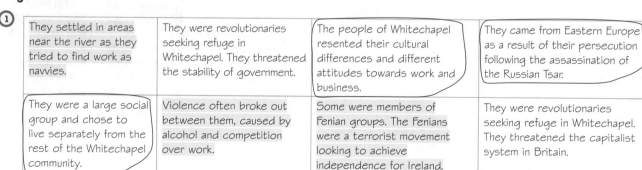

| | | | |
|---|---|---|---|
| They settled in areas near the river as they tried to find work as navvies. | They were revolutionaries seeking refuge in Whitechapel. They threatened the stability of government. | The people of Whitechapel resented their cultural differences and different attitudes towards work and business. | They came from Eastern Europe as a result of their persecution following the assassination of the Russian Tsar. |
| They were a large social group and chose to live separately from the rest of the Whitechapel community. | Violence often broke out between them, caused by alcohol and competition over work. | Some were members of Fenian groups. The Fenians were a terrorist movement looking to achieve independence for Ireland. | They were revolutionaries seeking refuge in Whitechapel. They threatened the capitalist system in Britain. |

**(2)** **a** A – c; B – a; C – d; D – b

**b** Student's own response.

## Page 14

**(3)** **a** Following up direct leads.

**b** Evidence from post mortems; Indirect leads from articles written by investigating journalists.

**c** Indirect leads from articles written by investigating journalists; soup kitchens.

**(4)** **a** Media          lack of forensic techniques

It was impossible to distinguish between animal and human blood.

Had to rely on clues such as clothing and people reporting missing persons to identify victims.

Police were sent over 300 letters and postcards by men claiming to be the murderer. Too many leads to follow up each effectively and took up police time.

If a witness gave a description police had no way of identifying the person described.

Bloodhounds were the only method of tracking criminals. Their was based on the dog's ability to track the smell of one person's blood through the streets of London.

Public accusations of Jewish and Irish people potentially led to greater disorder in Whitechapel, which the police would have to deal with.

**b** A – b; B – c; D – a, c; F – c

## Page 15

**(1)** Student's own response.

**(2)** A, B, D

**(3)** Student's own response.

## Page 16

**(1)** **police figures:** *The figures have been prepared by the police with great care...*
**convictions:** *The making of an attendance order...*
*was treated as a conviction by 121 police forces and excluded from the returns by 27. This alone added about 20,000 convictions a year to the tables, where there was in fact no conviction.*
**forensic investigation:** *The figures have been prepared...*

**(2)** Student's own response.

## Page 17

**(1)** How could you follow up Source D to find out more about the effectiveness of the use of bloodhounds in police investigations? In your answer, you must give the question you would ask and the type of source you could use.

**(2)**, **(3)** **a**, **b** and **c** Student's own response.

## Page 18

**(1)** **Highlight:** *It deprives it of a specially trained force of men with brainpower specially adapted for detective work...; ... the lack of local knowledge displayed by the police.*

**(2)**, **(3)** and **(4)** Student's own response.

## Page 19

**(1)** Student's own response.

# Unit 3

## Page 22

**(1)** Source C is useful to an enquiry into policing techniques as it tells us about the police looking for clues to the Ripper investigation whilst 'on the beat'. It describes how hard the police were working to try and solve the case, working through paperwork and completing searches. During the case, the police received over 300 letters and postcards from men claiming to be the murderer, all leads that they then had to spend time following up. We can assume that as a police officer working the case he was fully aware of the time individuals were putting into the investigation. However, his description is for an article being published in a newspaper so he may have wanted to create a sense of sympathy or support for the police by assuring the public they were doing their best to identify the murderer.

## Page 23

**(1)** Mug shots

**(2)** **a** Suggested content:

   i **Bertillon System:** photographs and measurements of all criminals and suspects were taken when arrested and then kept on file.

   ii **Mug shots:** photographs of front and side profiles of suspects and criminals.

   iii **Forensic:** scientific clues gathered at the crime scene.

   iv **Telephone boxes:** initially to improve communication between police forces or between the beat constable and headquarters.

**b** Student's own responses. Suggested answers: poor communications through forces, following up false leads from media, bloodhounds unable to effectively track smell through busy streets...

**(3)** **a** and **b** Early in investigation     After investigation

| Setting up soup kitchens to encourage witnesses to come forward. | Follow up on journalists' theories. | The Bertillon System. Taking photographic records and measurements of all suspects to keep on file. |
|---|---|---|
| By the end of the 19th century the Metropolitan Police were benefiting from the installation of telephone lines. | Using evidence from post mortems to gather clues as to the identity of the murderer (i.e. likely to be left-handed). | Following up on clues found with the victims to establish their identity and possible connections to their murderer. |

## Page 24

**(4)** **(a)** A – b; B – c; C – a

**(b)** Student's own response.

**(5)** **(a)** **Bertillon System:** recording measurements and photographs of suspects by the police to keep on record and use for identification purposes.

**Improvements in the environment of Whitechapel:** Every person has a unique DNA profile (the building blocks of life). This profile can be created and used to identify a suspect from hair, skin or bodily fluids.

**Telephone lines to police stations:** In a time before mobile phones, these were an effective way for beat constables to communicate with the rest of the force while out on the streets.

**(b)** A: b, d, e

B: c, f

C: a, b

## Page 25

**(1)** **What was the nature of the obstacles?** … prevent our working doubly over the same ground … in more constant communication with yours

**What techniques were the police using?** here every morning to consult or may I send an officer every morning to consult with your officers.

**Did they have any idea about why the murders were happening?** Nothing in source.

**Who within the police were involved in the investigation?** CID and Charles Warren (Police Commissioner).

**(2)** **What was the nature of the obstacles?** Not in source.

**What techniques were the police using?** Post mortem reports.

**Did they have any idea about why the murders were happening?** Desire to dissect, need of an organ (womb was missing).

**Who within the police were involved in the investigation?** Police coroner.

## Page 26

**(1)** and **(2)** Student's own response.

## Page 27

**(1)** and **(2)** Student's own response.

## Page 28

**(1)** and **(2)**

**Identifies content that is useful from Source A:**

*… Source A is useful to an enquiry into the difficulties the police faced in trying to capture the East End serial murderer because it implies that the police and CID were not communicating well enough. It also implies that this might be improved by sending an officer each morning to consult with the CID…*

**Identifies content that is useful from Source B:**

*… Source B is from the coroner's report of Dr Wynne Baxter into the murder of Annie Chapman so it is useful in showing us how the police were able to follow up the clues as a result of the post mortems…*

**Identifies an element of provenance that may be useful:**

*… A letter written in Source A in October 1888 is by Charles Warren, who was Police Commissioner and therefore he had first-hand experience of communications between uniformed police and the CID…*

**Identifies an element of provenance that may limit how the source is used:**

*… He might also be emphasising the efforts that the police force in Whitechapel were making in order to improve communications…*

**(3)** Student's own response.

# Unit 4

## Page 32

**(1)** Explain **one** way in which law enforcement in Anglo-Saxon Britain was the same as law enforcement in Norman Britain.

**(2)**, **(3)**, and **(4)**

> During Norman rule people continued to use hue and cry to enforce the law and track down possible criminals. This continued the law enforcement from the Anglo-Saxon period, when witnesses within the community were expected to alert the rest of their community when they saw a crime taking place so that the criminal could be caught and punished. This fitted in with the fact that people continued to live in small communities so law enforcement run by the community continued to make sense. If this responsibility was not taken on by the whole community, everyone would be fined. In Norman law this fine – Murdrum fine – was paid to the king's officials rather than the wergild of the Anglo-Saxon period, which was paid to the victim or victim's family.

## Page 33

**(1)** The desire to be more powerful **motivated**/impeded Norman kings to make punishments **harsher**/less **harsh**. For example, there was an increase in the number of crimes punishable by death or mutilation. This also applied to new laws and under the new Forest Laws **poaching**/slander was punishable by death. Norman kings also increased their control over law and order by making all fines payable to the **king's officials**/victim's family. The Normans, however, **continued**/ changed to use the hue and cry system to catch criminals as it **prevented**/encouraged villagers avoiding responsibility for law and order. The Norman system of law was based on the idea that all men should be safe from crime under the king's authority. This was called the king's Mund and it was a crime to disrupt this peace, much as it was in Anglo-Saxon law.

**(2)** A – e; B – a; C – d; D – f; E – c; F – b

## Page 34

**(3)** **a** and **b** Person    Property    Authority

| Theft | Arson | Disrupting the king's peace |
|-------|-------|------------------------------|
| Hue and cry | Murder | Murdrum fines payable to the king's officials. |
| Wergild payments to the victim's family | Poaching | Disrupting the king's Mund |

**(4)**

| Factor of influence | Example of new idea |
|---------------------|---------------------|
| King wants more control of law and order | Murdrum |
| The introduction of the feudal system | Murdrum |
| King wants to protect Normans against the Saxons | King's Mund |
| King wants exclusive hunting rights | Poaching |

## Page 35

**(1)** Explain **one** way in which types of crime in Anglo-Saxon Britain were similar to types of crime in Norman Britain.

**(2)** Explain **one** way in which punishments in Anglo-Saxon Britain were different from punishments in Norman Britain.

**(3)** Explain **one** way in which types of crime in Anglo-Saxon Britain were different from types of crime in Norman Britain.

**(4)** See questions **(1)**, **(2)**, **(3)**.

## Page 36

**(1)** Explain **one** way in which law enforcement in Anglo-Saxon Britain was different from law enforcement in Norman Britain.

**(2)**

| | A | B | C | D | E | F |
|---|---|---|---|---|---|---|
| Time parameter | (Normans but no Anglo Saxons or comparative words) | ✓ | (Anglo Saxons but no Norman or comparative words) | ✓ | ✓ | ✓ |
| Topic | ✗ | ✗ | | ✗ | ✗ | |
| Comparison focus | | ✗ | | | ✗ | |

## Page 37

**(1)** Tick:

Identified one difference?

Selected content knowledge for that difference for the first time period required?

Selected content knowledge for that difference for the second time period required?

**Do not tick:**

Explained how there is a similarity or a difference? –

They need a more direct comparison to fully explain the difference, i.e. the payment of the fine to the king's official rather than the victim or victim's family meant it was more about increasing the king's power and control than compensating victims. Due to the way the Normans had taken control, they probably felt they needed to establish this.

**(2)** One way in which punishments in Anglo-Saxon Britain were different from punishments in Norman Britain is that fines for failure to bring a suspect to justice were paid to the king's officials rather than to the victim or victim's family. During the Anglo-Saxon period these fines had been a form of compensation for the victim's loss.

**(3)** Student's own response.

## Page 38

**(1)** **Time period:** Anglo-Saxon – Norman

**Topic/theme:** punishments

**Comparison focus:** similarities

**(2)** During the Anglo-Saxon period mutilation and the death penalty were common punishments for those found guilty of a crime. The Normans continued to apply these punishments ~~although there were an increased number of crimes that were punishable by death, such as the new Forest Laws and in particular poaching.~~ Mutilation continued to take the form of branding or chopping off a body part as this ensured the community could identify the person as a criminal.

**(3)** **a** See crossed out text above.

**b** The text does not directly draw any similarity between punishments in Anglo-Saxon Britain and Norman Britain.

**(4)**

| Checklist | ✓ |
|-----------|---|
| Has the student: | |
| identified one similarity? | ✓ |
| selected content knowledge for that similarity for the first time period required? | ✓ |
| selected content knowledge for that similarity for the second time period required? | ✓ |
| explained how there is a similarity or difference? | ✓ |

**(5)** **Highlight:** continued, although, continued

## Page 39

**(1)** **a**, **b** and **c**

Explain **one** way in which the role of the community in Anglo-Saxon Britain was similar to the role of the community in Norman Britain.

**(2)**, **(3)**, **(4)**, and **(5)** Student's own response.

# Unit 5

## Page 42

① All except 'This is based on the continued belief that if a person knows they can be identified it will deter them from committing a crime. This is the same belief that hue and cry and the beat constable were based on'. – this is a continuity, not a change.

## Page 43

① prevent (solve)

| | |
|---|---|
| Breathalysers (1967) – allow police to test blood alcohol level immediately at the roadside – and **speed cameras** (1992). | Closed circuit television (CCTV) films people's movements in public areas. |
| **Improved communications** – a wider range of records are kept, which can be accessed at scene using new technologies like tablets and smartphones. | Increases in **data management** – for example, the DNA database, which in 2015 held the profiles of 5.7 million individuals. |
| Improvements in **forensic sciences** – forensic teams carry out detailed searches at crime scenes looking for decisive evidence such as DNA and fingerprints. | **Biometric screening** – records unique characteristics such as fingerprints or eye patterns to restrict access to owners and those with permissions. |
| **Mass video surveillance** – allows private companies and authorities to analyse large amounts of online behaviour to predict acts of terrorism and other criminal activity. | **Improved computer software** – can analyse large amounts of video footage very quickly to identify criminals. |

② Student's own response.

## Page 44

③ Student's own response but might include:

**Control actions:** ASBO; Electronic tagging

**Keep community safe:** ASBO; Electronic tagging

**Reform:** Community Service; Care orders; Drug and alcohol treatment programmes; Restorative justice

④ Student's own response but might include:

**ASBO:** If the person behaved inappropriately around certain people or in certain places they may stop if their access is restricted.

**Community service:** Tries to encourage a feeling of pride and responsibility in the community.

**Restorative justice:** If they can empathise with their victim and imagine how it might feel if they had that experience or had been treated that way they may consider the consequences of their behaviour more.

**Drugs and alcohol treatment programmes:** If their behaviour is affected by drugs or alcohol, being able to avoid these substances may change their behaviour.

**Electronic tagging:** This means they can live a relatively normal life in the community but knowing they are being monitored so they can experience living their normal lives while correcting their behaviour.

**Care orders:** A young person may commit an offence because of the environment in which they are being raised, or the way they are being raised. By monitoring, and where possible, changing and improving these conditions, young people are given more options than crime.

⑤ Student's own response but might include:

**1902:** Hard labour in prisons ended – a sign of the change in attitudes towards rehabilitation.

② Student's own response but might include:

**Relevant ideas: Specialist police units – Evidence 1:** Cyber crime with birth of the internet. Requires police forces with specialist training to monitor. **Evidence 2:** Requires specialist software to monitor.

**Relevant ideas: CCTV – Evidence 3:** The police have relinquished responsibility for monitoring most CCTV to private businesses.

**1922:** Increased focus on prisoner welfare. Separate system abolished and education opportunities introduced – education in prison can create greater opportunities to avoid further criminal activity at the end of a sentence.

**1933:** New focus on preparing prisoners for life after serving their sentence. Open prisons and day-release – proactively thinking about the prisoner's life outside of prison and what can be done to prevent them going back to criminal activity.

## Page 45

① Explain why there were <u>changes</u> in (law enforcement) in the period 1900 to the present.

②

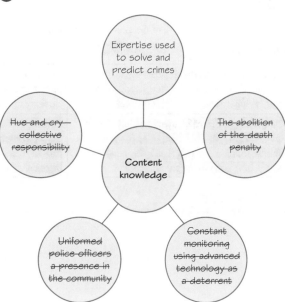

## Page 46

(1) (a) **Underline:** In order to detect and prevent these crimes the police have created specialist units, who can use their expert training to identify and disrupt trade before the drugs reach the public. To do this effectively they are now able to use new surveillance technologies to monitor the actions of suspects and forecast crimes.

(b) Specialist crimes require specialist skills to detect them effectively.

(2) Student's own response.

## Page 47

(1) **Cross out:** 'mass surveillance techniques' and 'Fraud squad set up in 1946 to protect and deal with the growing crime in business and the stock market.'

(2) Student's own response.

## Page 48

(1) (a) **Highlight:** In order to detect and prevent these crimes the police have created specialist units, which can use their expert training to identify and disrupt trade...; People convicted of dealing drugs can face a prison sentence...; similar specialist unit was also created during the 20th century to protect the growing stock market from associated financial and business crimes...; new surveillance technologies...

(b) **Underline:** In the 19th century, the beat constable would be responsible for ensuring law and order on the streets by being a uniformed presence among the community.

(2) Australia   Great Britain

| Ex-convicts were believed to be more likely to reoffend and were blamed for high crime rates in local towns. | Convict ships were inhumane according to some campaigners. | The gold rush had made Australia a desirable place to settle, so transportation was thought to be a less effective deterrent. | Convict workers meant lower wages or fewer available jobs for other locals. | People were concerned about running costs. | Up to the 19th century, prison had been used to house debtors and the accused in the run up to trial rather than as a punishment in its own right. As this purpose changed, more prisons were built in Britain. |

(c) **Circle:** ... suspect behaviour is recorded and those involved identified. Law enforcement has changed as a result of the nature of crime changing, and it is made more effective by the use of new technologies.

(d) **Situation before change:** crimes such as drug trafficking have increased in the period 1900 to the present

**Change made:** the police have created specialist units... new surveillance technologies

**Situation after change:** suspect behaviour is recorded and those involved identified

## Page 49

(1) **Topic/theme:** criminal activity

**Time parameters:** 1900 to the present

**Concept:** changes

(2) and (3) Student's own response.

# Unit 6

## Page 52

(1) (a) **Highlight:** Paragraphs 1 and 3

(b) **Circle:** Paragraph 2

(2) Student's own response.

## Page 53

(1) Student's own response.

## Page 54

(3) 1 = F; 2 = B; 3 = D; 4 = G; 6 = C; 5 = A; 7 = I; 8 = E; 9 = H

(4) c.1500–1700   c.1750–1900

| **Transportation** to the colonies – originally America and then following the war of independence to Australia. | **Public executions** to create spectacle and fear and act as a deterrent to crime. | **Mutilation** by branding the body or removing a digit or limb. |
| **Silent and separate systems** in prisons. Based on the belief that prison should involve hard work but that prisoners should be safe from one another. | **Fines** usually for breaking contracts or agreements or as compensation for damage caused to property or person. | **Pillory and stocks** punishment by public humiliation. Used for a wide variety of minor crimes such as dishonest shopkeeping or drunkeness. |

(5) Student's own response.

## Page 55

**①**  **a** and **b**

| Events | Changes |
|---|---|
| Oliver Cromwell became Lord Protector in 1653. | A number of 'moral crimes' were introduced to control behaviour. |
| Henry VIII closed down the monasteries. | More poor people were forced to find work in new towns, and were treated as vagrants. |
| | Vagrancy laws were brought in by the government. |
| The Game Act of 1671 was introduced. | Vagabonds were harshly punished. |
| The Heresy Acts were reintroduced by Mary I. | More people were burnt at the stake for heresy. |

## Page 56

**①** **a** 1500–1700 or 1900–present

**b** 1000–1500

**c** 1900–present

**d** 1000–1700

**②** Student's own response.

## Page 57

**①** Student's own response but examples below.

**Immediate impact:** Successful and therefore wealthy merchants in towns became visible targets for crimes like robbery.

**Impact on ideas:** Some people had enough money to hire their own private guards to protect them and their property.

**Widespread impact:** Between 1500 and 1700 the population of Britain increased by about 3 million.

**On-going impact:** Although the roles of town constable and night watchman had already been created, the force was expanded to cope with the rising crime rates.

**Long-term impact:** Town constables became the first professional (paid) law enforcers.

## Page 58

**①**

| Checklist | Paragraph 1 | Paragraph 2 | Paragraph 3 |
|---|---|---|---|
| Has identified a **change** rather than simply an event | ✓ | | ✓ |
| Is focused on **change** rather than **continuity** | ✓ | | ✓ |
| Has identified **why** the change is significant/ limited in significance | ✓ | ✓ | |

## Page 59

**①** Student's own response.

# Unit 7

## Page 62

**①**  **a** and **b**

| |
|---|
| Hopkins had been a lawyer who called himself the Witchfinder General... |
| ... when he set about... |
| ... hunting down witches. |
| In order to... |
| ... find potential witches Hopkins would encourage accusations based on suspicions. |
| ... therefore it was in Hopkins's interest to... |
| ... stir up hysteria and create as many 'leads' as possible.... When Hopkins died, |
| ... so too |
| did a lot of the rumour and hearsay of the witch hunts and there was a noticeable fall in prosecutions. |

**②** **Cause:** this meant that; in order to; creating the potential to; noticed the link between; in the hope of; this influenced

**Consequence:** as a result; it was not until

**Both:** increased the chances of; therefore; this contributed to; so too did

## Page 63

**①** **a** Economic problems; fear of vagabonds; reformation meant it was a crime against the King and state not just religious crime.

**b** Death of Matthew Hopkins or religious stability or enlightenment; Royal Society

**②** Student's own response.

## Page 64

**③**

| Rise | Decline |
|---|---|
| A, B, D | C, E, F |

**④** A – c; B – a; C – b

## Page 65

**①**

| this meant that | therefore | so too did |
|---|---|---|
| as a result | creating the potential to | in the hope of |
| in order to | this contributed to | this influenced |
| increased the chances of | noticed the link between | it was not until |

**②** **The middle answer:** Hopkins was a lawyer in Essex and East Anglia who called himself the Witchfinder General. He stirred up hysteria about witchcraft in the hope of finding as many witches as possible by encouraging people to make accusations based on suspicions. The financial rewards for each witch accused gave Hopkins the incentive to build superstitious attitudes as much as possible.

**(3)** Student's own response.

eg. There was a significant financial reward to people who successfully uncovered witchery. (1) It was in Hopkins's interest to stir up hysteria.

Choose a linking word to replace each number:

(1) This aims to link the the cause to the action – 'Therefore' for example.

## Page 66

**(1)** **a** **Circle:** As a result of...; Therefore...; Consequently...; Made possible...

**b** **Underline:** In addition...; In support of...; Furthermore...; Similarly...; Since...; For example...; Equally important...; Compared to...; Such as...; As well as...

**(2)** **a** 'therefore'

**b** 'as a result' keeps the meaning the same – student's own response.

**(3)** **a** In order to find potential witches, Hopkins would encourage accusations based on suspicions.

**b** Student's own response.

## Page 67

**(1)** **To compare and contrast ideas:** in contrast..., whereas..., however...

**To give examples of an idea:** For example..., such as...

**To show cause and effect:** as a result...; this hindered...; increased the chances of...; this motivated...; this contributed to...; noticed the link between...; in the hope of...; this influenced...

**(2)** B

**(3)** **a** **Underline:** One of the most significant reasons for the decline in superstitious attitudes and witchcraft was the death of self-styled Witchfinder General, Mathew Hopkins, who had whipped up hysteria for his own financial gain.

**b** Student's own response.

**c** Student's own response but an example might be: This **contributed** to the hysteria of the witch hunts and Matthew Hopkins was **motivated by** the financial gains. **As a result** when he died less witches were hunted.

**d** Student's own response but an example might be: **However** Matthew Hopkins was just one man hunting witches, his death did not change the opinion of the whole of society... / Although the financial rewards **increased the chances** of women being accused... / **In contrast**...

## Page 68

**(1)** **a , b**

The hysteria about witchcraft certainly went into decline after the death of Matthew Hopkins. Hopkins had been a lawyer who called himself the Witchfinder General when he set about hunting down witches in the east of England. In order to find potential witches Hopkins would encourage accusations based on suspicions. There was a significant financial reward to people who successfully uncovered witchery and this motivated Hopkins to stir up hysteria and create as many 'leads' as possible. People could receive the equivalent of a month's wages for each accused witch. When Hopkins died, therefore, so too did a lot of the rumour and hearsay of the witch hunts and there was a noticeable fall in prosecutions.

**c** Student's own response.

**d** Student's own response.

**(2)** Student's own response.

## Page 69

**(1)** and **(2)** Student's own response.

# Unit 8

## Page 72

**(1)** **Cross out:** 'did not'

**(2)** **Highlight:** Although we continue to use prisons to limit convicts' freedoms and as a deterrent to crime, conditions are much improved and rehabilitation, including alternatives to custodial sentences, is prioritised...

**(3)** Student's own response.

## Page 73

**(1)** A – c; B – d; C – a; D – b

**(2)** Student's own response but a suggestion might be:

**deterrent:** Aims to make you think it's a bad idea to commit the crime due to the undesirable nature of the consequences.

**rehabilitation:** Aims to help you to use training and support networks to reform your character and be able to function in society without committing crimes.

**(3)** Student's own response but a suggestion might be: Try to avoid custodial sentences for young people.

**(4)** Student's own response.

## Page 74

**(5)** Deterrent – pay back to society                Rehabilitation

| In 1907 probation officers were employed to check on offenders living outside of prison. | In 1933 New Hall in Wakefield was opened. This was the first open prison. Prisoners could take part in work programmes and gradually reintegrate into society. | In 1908 The Prevention of Crime Act created a national system of borstals for young offenders. They were very disciplined and structured but made time for work programmes and learning practical skills. |

| | | |
|---|---|---|
| Electronic tagging introduced in 1990s to control, monitor and limit the behaviour of offenders living outside of prison. | In 1969 a law was put in place which encouraged the courts to favour care orders and supervision by social workers for young offenders. | Restorative justice arranges a supervised meeting between offender and victim (or victim's family) to help offender understand the consequences of their actions. |
| Capital punishment existed until 1965, when it was abolished for all crimes except high treason (abolished in 1998). | Community service introduced in 1970s to improve local communities. | Anti-Social Behaviour Orders (ASBOs) place restrictions on where a person can go or with whom they can have contact. |
| Mass video surveillance allows the police and private companies to monitor online activity and CCTV to forecast acts of terrorism and crime. | In 1980s the government encouraged Neighbourhood Watch schemes to protect local communities through organised communication with the police. | Breathalysers and speed cameras catch and provide evidence of road crimes, leading to fines or possibly prosecution in court. |

**6** **a** Student's own response.

**b** Student's own response.

## Page 75

**1** **Change:** 'Prisons changed little in the period 1800–2000 as they were still intended to be a deterrent against crime. Life in prison continued to be made less desirable than living outside of prison.'

**Perception:** 'Despite humanitarian campaigns, change was relatively slow during the early 19th century.'

**Inspiration:** 'This is illustrated in the 1865 Prisons Act, which aimed to enforce a strict, uniform regime of punishment in all prisons.'

**Change and Longevity:** 'Freedoms were still severely restricted, and until the late 20th century there were no alternatives to incarceration.'

**2** **a** and **b** Student's own response.

## Page 76

**1** **a** and **b** Student's own response.

## Page 77

**1** **a**, **b** and **c** Student's own response.

**2** Student's own response.

## Page 78

**1** **a** Judgement 1: A

Judgement 2: A, B, C

Judgement 3: A, B

**b** Student's own response.

## Page 79

**1 2** and **3** Student's own response.

# Notes